BRIEF COMPANIONS

By *Joy Ufema*

Published in Fawn Grove, Pennsylvania
The Mulligan Company

Copyright © 1984 by Joy Ufema
All Rights Reserved.

Library of Congress Catalog Card Number: 84-61568

ISBN 0-930841-01-8

Dedicated to Mulligan,
who unconditionally loves me.

Much thanks to Roy and Georgia English for their support and encouragement all these years.

Thank you Walter and Josie Weir for time and energy and magnificent lunches accompanied by stimulating conversation.

Thank you Sylvia Dudley for trying.

And Steven Nierenberg, thank you for your magnificent business management, your forgiving heart, and those super Columbian cigars.

But most of all to Patty for helping me live through a very difficult time of pain and growth while undergoing much of the same herself.

TABLE OF CONTENTS

FOREWORD

The bad news is three out of four of us can expect to do our dying in some kind of medical institution. I find that information disconcerting. Since it matters more to me how I die than I die, I feel a vested interest as a mortal human being and as a nurse caring exclusively for terminally ill patients.

Brief Companions is not morose. It is a compilation of individuals, much like you and me, who have preceded us in taking leave of this planet. The lessons are from them. They tell us the value of honesty and sensitivity and the risk of caring.

I wrote this book as a legacy to all those patients so they can live on and continue to teach.

I want their living and dying to have an effect on many: the nurse in the cardiac unit, the physician in family practice, the questioning Clergy, the social worker, the hospice volunteer, the teenager in Iowa, the grandmother in Florida, and dying persons everywhere.

My work has meaning to me because I believe in helping the dying patient die his way. For the thousands of care-givers in this country, I want to offer courage to be open and honest.

The United States has been exposed to death teachers for the past two decades. I am still witnessing horror stories of patients not only having information withheld from them but actually being blatantly lied to about their diagnosis and prognosis.

We have not yet faced up to the facts of death and dying. What the academicians have done for us is teach us to intellectualize death. Until we are willing to relinquish words like "passed away" and "crossed over" and begin using honesty by calling death death, we will continue to ignore the impact dying has on each of us.

These semantics extend into our behavior attitude toward dying. The use of such euphemisims affect how we respond to dying persons. By sharing these stories of actual death-bed experiences, I am exposing the reader to realities of dying.

Mary Queen of Scots said "In my end is my beginning." The good news is you don't have to die to learn the lessons about living.

IT ALL STARTED WHEN

S TANDING IN FRONT OF A LARGE MAHOGANY DESK, I WAITED
  nervously while the Director of Nurses signed her name to
  some very important-looking documents.

My student-nurse uniform felt too tight and I was having
difficulty breathing. The room was becoming too small and
warm.

Shifting from one foot to another I studied her. She appeared
matronly. Her stiff-starched white uniform contributed to the
image of large, cool, unapproachable authority. My gaze was
drawn to the four badges and college pins decorating her lapels.
Her hair was graying and cut short. With poise she rose and
simply said, in a clear and firm voice, "You're out."

"Excuse me?" I stammered.

"Out. You've failed Drugs and Solutions, so you're out."

"You mean *out* out? No capping or anything?"

"I'm sorry, Joy. You just didn't cut it." She was direct yet kind.
I wasn't devastated, just surprised.

"But, Miss Berger," I pleaded, "I really want to be a nurse."

"I understand, Joy, but you don't seem to want it badly
enough to work for it. No one is going to hand it to you on a silver
platter."

Twelve years and many jobs later I was finally celebrating
successfully passing the State Board Examinations to become a
Registered Nurse. During that time I had worked as a dentist's
assistant, a nurse's aide, a psychiatric aide, and a Licensed Practical Nurse. I had picked grapes for Welch's, milked cows by hand,

and painted fences. But I never lost my burning desire to be a nurse; to have enough clout to function as an effective advocate for the vulnerable patient. I started taking night classes, then finally got accepted at Harrisburg Area Community College where I enrolled in a two-year program to earn an Associate Degree and become a nurse.

I was 29 when I graduated and chose to practice nursing at Harrisburg General Hospital. Over 100 years old, it looks over the Susquehanna River, and houses 450 beds.

I was working full-time on the evening shift on the urology floor. My patients consisted mostly of middle-aged males who, for the first time in their lives, were having difficulty voiding. I enjoyed my work and looked forward to the challenge of offering skilled comfort to suffering humanity.

Slowly things started to change. I suppose mostly it was that I was changing but also my fellow-nurses' attitude toward me. At first, it was judgmental.

"Ufema, the night shift is complaining because you're not done with charts till after midnight."

"Ufema, how come you didn't mark down whether or not Mr. DeFranco had a bowel movement? Huh? What are you doing?"

"He was upset about his biopsy, so I just sat and talked with him."

"Well, you better quit the talking and get on with business."

Mr. DeFranco was a 58 year old who had been admitted to the hospital because he was bothered with urinary difficulties. He complained of difficulty starting his "stream" and for the past year, needed to void three or four times during the night.

The prostate gland surrounds the neck of the bladder and urethra, and is present only in males. Common in his age group, the gland increases in size actually constricting the urethra and restricting the flow of urine. When the additional cells are nonmalignant, this condition is referred to as benign prostatic hypertrophy.

Unfortunately, in too many males, the cells are cancerous and can invade the bladder and pelvis; certainly justifying concern.

Around 10:30 p.m. when I was making a last check on my

thirty patients, I had found Angelo DeFranco sitting on the edge of his bed, in the dark. He was running his hands through his black wavy hair.

"Mr. DeFranco, you seem worried. Feel like talking?" I inquired.

"Oh, Mother of God, I'm so upset! My gland, you know, down there," he said, pointing at his genitals.

Earlier that morning he had gone to the little operating room to have a metal scope with a light inserted into his penis. The urologist would then snip a small piece of tissue from his enlarged prostate gland to send down to the laboratory for analysis.

At the nurses' station, on the desk, by the intercom machine, in a box marked Daily Reports was a blue sheet of paper, 8½" × 11", with Angelo DeFranco's future neatly typed upon it. I was aware that it had been sent to our floor but had been too busy to look at it.

"Just a moment, Angelo. I'll be right back."

It didn't matter to me what the results were; what mattered was that he was distraught over the unknown. Even if the news was bad, knowing would be preferable.

When man does not know what the truth is, he conjures up what he believes it must be; that conjuring is usually worse than the actual truth.

I hurried back to his room with the blue paper in hand. I pulled the curtain separating the two beds then turned on the low light.

"Angelo, get your specs."

"What you gonna do, Nursie?"

"I have something for you to read."

With shaking hands he put on his glasses, then studied the pathology report.

"You see, here," I began. "Your name?"

"Yes."

"And here, your room — 464?"

"Yes."

"And here, your doctor?"

"Yeh! Yeh!"

"Now, Angelo, look at this word."

He followed my finger with his.

"Be-ni-gen. Be-ni-gen. What is be-ni-gen?"

"Benign, Angelo. Do you know what benign means?"

"No, oh, Mother of God. I don't know!"

"It means OK. Your gland is OK."

He sat motionless.

Slowly he removed his glasses and very gently placed them in the drawer. He returned the blue paper, then looked at me. A big grin crept across his wonderful Italian face.

"Nursie, thank you."

He lay down still smiling, and I covered him up. As I stood in the doorway, I heard him whisper.

"God bless you, Nursie."

"God bless you, Angelo."

To me, this was nursing. True, I didn't seem to be able to "cut corners" as I was expected to do. Frequently, at 9 p.m., an R.N. from a medical-surgical floor downstairs would visit me. She would plunk herself down at the nurse's station, sipping a coke, and announce that she was on break.

"How do you do it?" I asked in amazement.

"Do what?"

"How do you manage to get all of your thirty patients taken care of and tucked in by 9 o'clock while I'm still running around here with a long way to go?"

"It's easy," she said, tearing into a bag of potato chips. "I just do the essentials. I mean like, if they've had a stroke or something I just roll 'em on their side, put a pillow behind 'em, pull the covers up and turn out the light."

"What about back care, and mouth care?"

"Hey, Ufema, who's gonna know? I mean, they had a stroke, so who're they gonna tell? Who's to know?"

"I'd know," I said firmly and walked away.

She shouted after me, "Yeh, you'll know. Do you also know you're never gonna make it in this business!"

Months later I received my evaluation from the Head Nurse.

"You're just not an efficient worker, Joy."

"I know I don't work as rapidly as others, but it's tough to get everything done when I only have one other helper."

"That's just it. You're not expected to get everything done; just the essentials. If somebody is in pain, give him a shot of Demerol and get on with your work. You don't need to sit and hold their hands, Ufema; give them a shot to settle down."

"Many times sitting and talking is just as effective as Demerol," I said.

"But not as efficient. It takes a minute to give the injection and then you can be out of the room and doing your charts. You're not going to try to tell me that you can settle someone down by *talking* for a minute!"

"Well, not usually, but . . ."

"No buts. We're talking efficiency here. You're just not cutting corners fast enough. I'm not going to recommend a raise. You understand, don't you?"

"Oh, sure, I'm beginning to understand real well."

Weeks after, I was driving home from work, sobbing. I was angry with myself for being so naive. I was equally angry with the nursing faculty at the college for not preparing me adequately for the real world of nursing. I was infuriated with hospitals for their dishonesty. Realistically, they simply are big businesses. OK, just admit it publicly. We can accept it. Instead, the administration professes human and humane care, "the patient comes first" credo. Just that day I was given Report from the nurse in charge who had personally only visited half of the patients on that floor. She was telling me of their condition according to what someone told her. I was angry with third party reimbursers for paying exorbitant medical bills when some patients did not see a Registered Nurse that day. I was angry and decided to do something about it.

I recalled seeing an announcement on the bulletin board about a coffee klatch meeting for any nurses with Miss Donovan, the Director. Prior to reporting on duty, I signed up to attend.

Mostly the discussion centered around requests for more vacation days, inquiries regarding free parking permits, and whether or not nurses' aides were qualified to monitor blood pressures.

I interrupted, introduced myself and asked, "Since there are eleven student nurses assigned on my urology floor during the day shift, why can't one or two of them be assigned evenings to help?"

Tall and stately Miss Donovan stared at me over her glasses. Small, warm, brown eyes revealed a slight twinkle of interest.

"Miss Ufema, student nurses' education no longer requires rotation of shift duty."

"I see. Then why not assign one or two of the hired staff from day shift to help out in the evening? With all the students on, the crew is literally stumbling over each other."

"Miss Ufema, surely you're not insinuating that a third-year nursing student is comparable in value to a Licensed Practical Nurse?"

"Yes, I am. Besides, I need more help and it seems stupid to me to have seventeen people on day shift and three on evenings."

"Stupid, you say?"

"Yes."

"Evening shift does not require the same amount of help since there are less duties. One example is meals. The day nurses have to serve breakfast *and* lunch. On 3–11 p.m. you only have to serve dinner."

"Plus a snack."

"Of course," she said, "the little snack."

"It's academic, Miss Donovan," I implored. "I still have to pass trays to thirty patients, twice with a lot less help."

"True," she conceded "however, you don't have to give baths to everyone or make rounds with doctors."

"Plenty of doctors come in till eight o'clock, plus I have fresh post-operative patients and many families with tons of questions."

"I'm afraid we've run out of time, ladies. Thank you all for coming."

Dismissed and a bit bewildered, we filed out silently.

Later that afternoon events converged into a Mexican stand-off.

After the coffee-klatch fun, I went directly to my floor. Consulting the schedule I learned the following information:

LPN — Regular day off
Aide — Called in sick
Ward Secretary — to rotate between three floors.

The *good* news was that an RN was to remain on duty till 5 p.m. to help pass supper trays. After that, I would be totally alone with thirty patients.

The lay-out of the C-building was exactly that, a C. A separate structure attached to the main hospital by a ramp, it once served as the student nurses' residence. The first floor housed gynecology patients, mostly ambulatory and short-stay. The second floor was psychiatric, third floor medical-surgical and the fourth was urology. Each floor was an exact replica of the other. Walking from the main building up the ramp through double doors one was suddenly on urology. Off this short corridor were patient rooms. A sharp right turn revealed a longer hallway with the nurses' station halfway. Another sharp right brought you to a short corridor with a blind end.

The patients' call lights were only lights. There was no bell. Consequently, if I was in a room off any of the corridors, I could not tell if the patient's light was on around the corner. Unlike the other seven floors of the main building which were huge, long hallways.

Slamming the schedule book shut, I reached for the phone and was soon speaking directly to one of the three evening supervisors. I explained my situation, then requested a RN from another station to work with me from 5 p.m. till 11 p.m. Her response was she had no one, and I had better accept it and get on with my work.

With great control, I called the Director of Nurses, Miss Donovan.

She was a bit sympathetic, reminding me that on numerous occasions in large Philadelphia hospitals she, too, worked an entire floor alone.

My reply was that just because she did it did not make it right.

"And furthermore, Miss Donovan, I consider being alone on this floor *unsafe* nursing care. Unless you get me help by 5 I'm leaving. I refuse to accept this absurd responsibility."

"Let me make myself perfectly clear," her voice raising, "if you walk out, I'll see to it that you lose your license and never practice nursing again in Pennsylvania."

"Miss Donovan, this is *not* practicing nursing. I'm making a statement by walking out. If I remained on duty under these unsafe circumstances, I'm condoning the situation and it will continue to exist."

"It's like a rat jumping from a sinking ship," she said curtly.

"Miss Donovan, I'm not spending any more time discussing this. As respectfully to you as I can, I'm announcing that I'll leave the hospital at 5 unless you send me another person."

"You walk out, and you can keep on walking."

"Thank you," I said, "Goodbye."

Coolly, I received Report from the day shift while student nurses stood around, giggling, arguing over prize pieces of chocolate candy donated by a discharged and grateful patient.

Around 4:45, while distributing the evening meal, one of the house supervisors came up the ramp with Mrs. Henry, a Registered Nurse from M-7.

The supervisor dropped her off at the nurses' station and left.

"Man, am I glad to see you!" I beamed.

"Listen, Ufema, I don't know if I'm so glad to be here, but, what the hell, let's get to it."

We worked hard and unceasingly. I called down to the kitchen for two extra trays, and we took turns eating at the desk and manning the phone.

By 11 p.m. all patients were present and accounted for, safe and relatively sound. I slapped Mrs. Henry on the back.

"Thanks a lot, you helped me win a big battle here tonight."

"You're welcome, Joy, but just because you won this battle doesn't mean you're gonna win the war."

Little did I know, the war was just beginning.

"WHAT'S A DEATH AND DYING NURSE?"

I T WAS A BEAUTIFUL SPRING DAY. I WAS RETURNING FROM BALTI-
more where I had attended a seminar taught by Dr. Elisabeth
Kubler-Ross. She spoke as a physician from Switzerland
who practiced medicine among people who accepted death as a
natural part of life. After moving to the United States, she was
amazed at our death-dying attitudes. I listened with undivided
attention as she challenged each of us to stop isolating our dying
patients and accept the terminally ill person as our teacher.

I learned from her the value of finding out from the patient
what we can do to help him die with peace and dignity. She was
terribly moving in a quiet way. I listened well, wrote pages of
notes, and thanked her for being a mentor we nurses badly
needed.

I was so inspired that I pulled over to the nearest phone booth
and called the nursing office at the hospital requesting an appointment with Miss Donovan.

The following afternoon I stood before her. Seated behind the
familiar mahogany desk (earlier memories crept in) she placed
her signature on a few memoranda then looked up, over her
glasses. Her manner was a bit stiff but her eyes were warm. (I was
positive I detected that old twinkle.)

"Well, spit it out! What do you want *this* time?"

"I want to be the Death and Dying Nurse," I said firmly.

"You what?"

I repeated my request.

"Well, what indeed would this Death and Dying Nurse do?"

I shared with her details of the seminar then explained briefly about the benefit to patient, family, and staff to have a special nurse who was assigned exclusively to terminally ill persons, especially for counseling. It would be an extra benefit to those special patients to have me available without the pressures of regular floor duty.

"Besides, Miss Donovan, remember Kubler-Ross's challenge."

"You know we're dealing with an unknown quantity here. I'm not quite sure how to go about it, but I think it's worth the risk."

"You, you do?" I stammered.

"Yes, I do. Keep this under your hat till I can lay some groundwork. During the next few months you might come up with a job description."

"Months? I had hoped we could implement this in the next few weeks."

"Miss Ufema," she said, removing her glasses. "It will require some amount of proper timing and preparation if we want this to be successful."

"Right. Thanks a lot."

Six weeks passed and all systems were very close to "go."

There remained one minor obstacle. The entire plan was contingent upon a replacement.

Harrisburg Hospital School of Nursing was graduating the last class of students in June. Having become quite friendly with several of the girls, I inquired from Marie what her future plans might be.

"Well, my boyfriend has another year of college so I guess I'll work here at the hospital."

I snapped to attention.

"Hey! That sounds great!"

"Yeh, we heard they were going to hire about fifteen new graduates," she said.

"Gee," I urged, "maybe you better get your application submitted. Any special unit you'd like?"

"Well, this might sound crazy, but *you'll* understand."

"What, Marie?"

"I really like urology. I'd like to work right here."

"Oh," I said, attempting to remain cool. "I do understand. This is a great floor to start on. You'd *love* it."

Every few weeks I would casually inquire from Marie whether she had made application for employment.

"Oh, man, no, I've been so busy with finals and graduation."

"Well, you better set up an interview, at least, so they know you're interested. You know the Associate Degree nurses are graduating this month and a lot of them will probably choose urology." We both knew I was lying.

Finally, late one afternoon, I ran into Marie in the library.

"Hey, Joy, *great* news!"

My heart soared (Death and Dying, here I come!)

"Chuck and I are getting married!" Oh, no! My heart sank.

"Yeh, that's great, when?"

"Next month, the 25th."

"Oh, nice. What are your plans?"

"Shoot, I forgot to tell you the other neat thing. I had my interview with Miss Donovan and she assigned me urology — evenings — we'll be working together!"

"Hey, that's great! Listen, I gotta run — congratulations — I'm *really* happy for you." (And for me!")

The next month, July, 1973, I began.

During the morning of that first day, I had visited about five terminally ill patients. In my hand I carried cards identifying each patient most of which was quite personal. The cards were too large to fit in my uniform pocket, so over lunch, I ran downtown to the local five and dime store and quickly purchased a notebook in which the cards could fit.

I was standing at the elevator, waiting to go to the eleventh floor where there are only private rooms. When patients with leukemia are in danger of infection, due to their drastically reduced quality of white blood cells, they are placed in single rooms in reverse isolation. A cold germ, transmitted by staff or visitors could be deadly since their condition is so severely compromised.

Approaching me was a fellow nurse from urology. There is a

joke about working on urology. "Once you have earned the "yellow shoes" award you probably have gleaned all the nursing knowledge there is on the subject.

Standing in her yellow shoes she said, "Hey, Joy, I see you're really taking this new job seriously."

"Of course I am, but what do you mean?"

"Well, the black book!"

I looked down at the notebook, and for the first time realized I had unconsciously chosen not red or green but a *black* notebook. (I'm sure Freud would have some opinion about my decision.)

Riding to the eleventh floor, my thoughts were focused on the associations we all have of death and how they can get in the way. Black is a common color used to depict grief and bereavement. Wearing a black arm-band for thirty days said to everyone, "be gentle with me, I'm painful."

I stopped at the nurses' station and began leafing through the cardex. Suddenly I came across the name of a woman I had known when I was a student in college and working during the summer at a local hospital where she was a patient. She had been a dentist from Latvia. While I tended to her incision for gall bladder surgery, she shared stories with me of escape from Russia in the early 1940's. I had certainly grown attached to her and her family, but we had lost touch for over a year.

Flipping the care plan open, I read her diagnosis: lymphosarcoma. It stunned me and I thought how matter-of-factly the ward secretary wrote the word. How unkind to have that proper noun appear opposite the name of someone I knew and loved.

I was afraid to see her. I've since then learned that it's okay to be afraid. Fear is real. I think we expend a lot of energy running from things we fear, especially death. My heart got me into her room, not my feet. She looked exactly the way I feared. We hugged a little bit and cried a little bit—because she knew I knew.

"So, you're finished with school and now you're a real nurse. Are you working on this floor now or what are you doing?"

"Well," I hesitated, "as a matter of fact, I've just started a new job today. I'm working with patients who are seriously ill."

"Oh, my," she said. "I guess you won't be my nurse this time."

"Probably not," I replied, uncomfortably.

I assisted her back to her bed. While tucking the covers around her frail frame she looked directly in my eyes and asked, "What's in the black book?"

Oh, names of people who are seriously ill," I stammered.

"Then, you do have my name"—more a declaration than a question.

"Yes," I replied, honestly.

I gave her a goodby kiss. As I got to the door she called out, "Joy, promise you won't give me any *bad* news!"

"I promise."

I quickly slipped down the back stairway, crying. First, because I was losing a friend and secondly, because it came to me again, I too must die, and some days that fact is not at all okay with me. But, that's OK, too, because that's real.

The lesson here is that she has never died before so she needs to do this her way. She's probably coping with the stress of death the way she coped with the stress of life. "Don't tell me any bad news." She has the right to choose that same mechanism now. I walked slowly down the back steps to the fourth floor. Entering his room I found Mr. Wilson lying flat in bed, looking emaciated and very jaundiced. Despite the tangled mass of tubes from every orifice, he moved over to make room for me to sit.

Taking his hand, I simply asked, "Mr. Wilson, my name is Joy. I wonder if you feel like sharing with me what it's like being seriously ill."

I gave something to this man no one else had given. I gave him, with that one question, a sense of control in a very uncontrollable situation. By asking him if he *feels* like sharing, I allow him an actual choice. He has few. Both his life and his disease are out of control. He must eat only during those hours that the kitchen is open, he is bothered by three roommates who have blaring radios, cigars, and laughing friends. For 63 years this man took a shower every night. Now he is subjected to every morning with tepid, too soapy water by a nurse who refuses to tell him her first name or his blood pressure figures.

"Do you *feel* like sharing?" That simple. If he would have said no, I would have honored that. (Out of 1,000 patients, 2 said no.)

"Do you feel like sharing *what?*"—About what it is like being *seriously* ill. Not terminally ill. Seriously ill. This still allows some hope for the patient while providing me with a subject matter that is not too threatening for the patient and allows me to learn *from him* what his perception of the situation actually is.

"Seriously ill" also differentiates me from neighbors, clergy, and kin who only want to talk about the Phillies or their new car.

I am telling the patient that I am comfortable with the language of death and dying. He may *choose* to cooperate in the "pretend everything is all right" game with everyone else but, from the start, he now knows I'm different. If he wants to talk about *anything* I am willing to stay and listen and share. I'm different from all the rest. I've let him know he can take advantage of that difference any time he chooses.

"Do you feel like sharing with me what it's like being seriously ill?"

"Well," he said, softly, "I know I ain't gettin' out of here alive, if that's what you mean."

"Yes, that's what I mean. How do you know that? Did the doctors tell you?"

"No," he said, with a little chuckle. "They don't tell me nothing. How I know is I can't walk to the bathroom by myself no more."

I couldn't help thinking how smug many physicians, nurses, and spouses can be when they're so sure that the individual died without even knowing he was dying!

Mr. Wilson knew in a very down-to-earth, human way. He didn't require some specialist waltzing in announcing that his SMA_{12} blood test reveals elevated LDH and SGOT! He knows, in his own unique, yet natural, way.

"No," he said, "they don't even come in here and bother to ask how I feel."

(A classic opener, *if* you're listening.)

"Mr. Wilson, how *do* you feel?" I asked.

"Not too damn good," he said.

"Have you shared any of these feelings with your Mrs.?"

"Nope, I don't know if you ever seen her. She's one of them Italians, only stands about five feet tall. I don't know for sure if she could take this."

Searching for past coping mechanisms, I asked what other crises they had shared."

"Well, I was in WWII."

"Yes."

"And, we had a still-born baby," his eyes filled with tears.

Since we are fairly predictable in our utilization of coping mechanisms during crises I was interested in learning from him how he handled past problems. I could, hopefully, help him utilize his coping pattern that was useful for those events to assist him through his current situation.

"Mr. Wilson, how did you and Mrs. Wilson get through those times?"

"I don't know," he said, "I guess we just held on to each other and talked it through."

"Yes, and don't you think holding each other and talking is the best thing to do now? I'm afraid this is the worst crisis you and your wife are ever going to share."

"Yeah, you're right," he said, almost enthusiastically. "Say, would you come around later when she comes in to visit?"

"You bet."

As we sat in the coffee shop, I asked Mrs. Wilson how sick her husband was.

"Oh, dear," she whispered, "he's dying."

"Yes, I know, he told me today."

"He *told* you?"

"Yes, but he felt he needed to keep it from you."

"But, I've known all along. I asked the doctor not to tell him — I didn't think he could take it."

"He said the same thing about you. After talking with both of you, I think it's time to bring all of this out in the open. How would you feel about that?"

"Well, I'm a little bit afraid." She started to cry. "But you know, dear, I surely do love him."

"That sounds good enough to get you two through this. Come on, he's waiting."

After seating Mrs. Wilson in a comfortable chair at her husband's bedside, I pulled the heavy, yellow curtain around them.

I promised to return in an hour, and when I did I found her leaning her head on his pillow and both of them were weeping. Also, I saw that the whole cloud of pretense had disappeared and, together, they were discussing who gets the gun cabinet and plans to bring Jeff home from Colorado.

None of us can stop this disease that is going to take this man's life. But we *can* help make *some* sense of worth out of this tragedy by helping *him* take some control over the remainder of his life, regardless of the amount of time left.

NOTHING FROM THE HEART
IS EVER WRONG

For entertainment I especially enjoy watching the television show "Little House On The Prairie". During one particular segment, Pa was teaching Laura about life. She was seeking a set of rules that would be applicable in all situations. She implored him to tell her how she could always be sure of saying and doing the right thing. He responded quite simply, "Darlin', nothin' from the heart is ever wrong."

I'm requested by many Lauras in the nursing profession to give them a few pat answers in dealing with dying patients. They want to know a handy response to use for each person everytime they talk about death.

"When the patient says *that,* you say *this!*"

How terribly clever. It's all so comfortably predictable. The problem arises, however, when Nurse Laura forgets her memorized speech and ends up repeating her lines from the beginning like a child in the school play. The dying patient senses the unnaturalness the nurse is feeling and, in a sensitive way, protects her from any further discomfort by changing the subject. Relieved, the nurse falsely interprets that her responses were effective. Therefore, she repeats her scene for the next patient.

A hospital chaplain once remarked to me, "I'm never totally at ease when I enter a dying patient's room. That's a good sign, though, because it keeps me from getting over-confident."

I disagree. How much more effective he could be by simply being himself. He may argue—"Then the patient will see I'm uncomfortable and he won't have trust in my ability to help him."

I contend patients read our discomfort accurately and clearly every time we exhibit it. The role of "super-human" keeps creeping in. Why do we feel we have to be all things to all people?

You'll read it in subsequent chapters — the answer to dealing with life and death is simply be real. That means be honest about all of your feelings all of the time. I believe we have a responsibility to ourselves and our fellow humans to be real.

The following story is about a case that I didn't handle well regarding my choice of words and how I rectified that situation by being honest.

At Harrisburg Hospital there is a team of nurses who specialize in stomal therapy. Their work is exclusive to those individuals who have a part of the intestine brought through the surface of the skin on the abdomen, like a colostomy.

The team leader, Joanne, gave me the new referral.

He was 44 years old and worked in the steel mill.

I walked into his room and simply introduced myself as Joy. The patient dismissed his visitors, turned off the television, then motioned for me to sit down beside him on the bed.

"Mr. Prescott, the nurses from the stoma team asked me to have a chat with you."

"That's fine. What would you like to talk about?"

"Well, I work exclusively with patients who have cancer, and I . . ."

"Cancer! Hey, I don't have *cancer* do I?"

"Yes, Mr. Prescott, you do."

"Oh my God!" he said, "I can't have cancer!"

"Mr. Prescott, I'm terribly sorry. I thought you knew. I just feel awful."

"Oh God, not cancer. My doctor never said anything about cancer!"

"What did he say?"

"Well, he operated on me and gave me this colostomy."

"Did he tell you why you have to have it?"

"Yeah. He said I had an abscess."

"I see."

"But now that I think back about all of this, I can start putting it together. See, last summer I was having trouble making my bowels work, and I was vomiting and stuff and had a lot of pain. Then this colostomy doesn't work and I'm vomiting and have that same pain."

"What do you make of that?"

"Well, if I have cancer *now*, I must have had it last year too, huh?"

"I'm afraid so, Mr. Prescott. How do you feel about that?"

"Not very damn good."

"I feel bad about telling you. I'm sorry that you had to learn it that way."

"It's not your fault," he said gently, "I'm just glad I know the truth. Please stay with me now and just hold my hand for a while. I want to tell you about the four year old daughter I have to leave behind."

I sat on his bed, held his hand, looked directly into his eyes and gave him my undivided attention.

He talked for over an hour. We shared what it means for both of us, as mortal human beings, to *have* to die. We shared about how flip it can be to hear people merely mouth the words "death is a part of life; it's natural."

After being assured that he would not jump out of the window, I left.

As I returned to my office I was aware of learning a new lesson. Life doesn't have pat answers for all the questions. Frequently we must make judgments with limited information. Sometimes our decisions are poor ones with serious complications.

The best way to deal with these situations is to acknowledge our error and, if possible, include the patient in the repair work. I even recommend discussing openly how the patient would have preferred the conversation to have occurred.

I worry that the more degrees we acquire and the more prestigious our position becomes the more uptight we get about making mistakes. We tend to hide behind our lab coats and clipboards exuding an aloof aura that protects our thin skin. This gets in the way of meaningful *dialogue.*

We need to be secure enough in our fallibility as human beings to learn from each other, especially from our patients. Frequently, it is they who are the teachers.

DEAD BABIES MAKE ME CRY

IT WAS SUMMER AND QUITE HOT WHEN A CASE ONE WAS ANnounced over the hospital public address system. CASE ONE are code words signifying a patient has suffered either cardiac or respiratory arrest and all available medical and nursing personnel is requested to rush to assist.

This particular crisis was taking place in the Emergency Room. Leaving my office I ran down seven flights of stairs. In front of the double doors I saw a young black woman pacing back and forth, wringing her hands, and screaming,

"Oh, dear God! I think my baby's dead! I didn't kill my baby! Oh, my God! I think my baby's dead!"

I sat her down but she kept screaming and crying.

"Just wait here a minute," I commanded, "and I'll be right back to tell you what's happening."

I went in and people were washing their hands and putting instruments away.

I asked, "What's happened?"

One of the nurses said, "He's dead—the baby's been dead a couple of hours. A crib death."

In the meantime, her 18 year old husband got there yelling and punching, "My son, somebody has killed my son."

Things were getting pretty wild out in the waiting room.

So I said, "I've got the young parents here. Who's going to come out with me?" One of the female residents on Pediatrics said she had to start rounds, and departed. A Pakistani resident said, "Miss Ufema, my English, no good." So he split. A dead baby is very painful. No one wants to be involved. I went back out to the waiting room.

"My baby, my baby's dead, isn't he?", the mother said.

"Yes, that he is."

"Oh my God. Oh my God. I didn't kill him. I didn't kill him. I fed him and I was watching "The $10,000 Pyramid" and I went back up to check on him and he was dead."

Then she said, "My baby, I've got to see my baby." I told her okay but to wait a second, that I'd be right back. The head nurse and I put a little clean undershirt and diaper on him and he was just beautiful. I brought them in, and the young husband was holding up his wife. We were all standing around with the cubicle curtains closed, crying. The Daddy went over and picked up his baby. In a resuscitative way, he covered his little mouth and nose with a kiss in an attempt to breathe life back into him. I was not going to stop this, although we all felt very uncomfortable and wanted to leave. Yet they needed unobtrusive support. Then he thrust the baby into my arms in an attempt to have me fix him. When I couldn't, he punitively took him from me, and gave him to Val, his wife, as if saying, "You gave him life, my God, do it again." She was wailing, verging on fainting. The young father's immediate grief needed all the time and space that we could give him. It only took him a couple more minutes before he put the baby back on the litter — a huge litter and a little tiny infant. And he covered him with a sheet.

He said, "Come on, Val, there is nothing more we can do here."

He asked me to get them a cab, and I said of course. We went out through the double doors into the main area of the emergency ward. Val was still wailing and screaming quite demonstratively. A cute little nurse with a uniform way above her knees and a blond ponytail sticking out of the hole in her cap, came up the hall, waving a syringe, because Val was too loud and disturbing everybody. She said she was going to give her a shot. When Val asked what she was doing, the nurse said she had to draw blood for a test.

"No, wait," I said, "Val, it's a sedative, if you want it." "No," she said, "I'm all right." Although she was weeping, she was behaving very normally.

The nurse said, "Well, what should I do with this? I already drew it up and signed it out."

"Why don't you give it to yourself? Maybe that would help," I replied.

I took them out and said to the cab driver, "Take these kids home and don't charge them a penny, they just lost their baby." Saluting me, he replied, "I'll do it, nurse, I'll do anything you tell me."

Death affects cab drivers, too. Perhaps he had a baby at home and was fearful that his little child could die.

Thirty days later I reminded myself to check on Val.

I would have preferred to call her on the telephone but she didn't have one. I didn't want to, but I made a home visit. I didn't want to see the baby's crib or the box of Pamper Disposable Diapers, but neither did she.

We both cried a little. I just sat quietly while she told me again how it happened and what she did and how she felt. This was her way of working through grief.

I've visited her since many times. She has conceived and delivered another baby boy. He's two years old now and just fine.

I believe she represents the epitome of risk-taking. Life holds no guarantees. She risked bearing another child and losing him to Sudden Infant Death Syndrome, for the chance to hold and nurture and love, for who knows how short a time.

But isn't that what caring is? Risking. All of us choose to become involved, lose our hearts, and risk feeling pain. I think that's what nursing and medicine are all about. We don't have to experience the loss of a child to be able to empathize. We can, however, choose to be companions with those who *are* in pain for the potential tragedy of death exists for each of us.

The next case history is also about a very brave woman who chose to risk losing a part of herself. She had lost five pregnancies in the past nine years.

I lost, too. A very large part of my heart.

"Joy, this is Marlene up on OB. Could you come up real quick?

We have a problem."

Both my mind and my feet raced up the steps. Obviously the only two problems that could possibly occur in Obstetrics was either a dead baby or a dead mother. I wasn't too brave about either.

Marlene nervously gave me the story. During the night, this very tall, beautiful black woman had delivered a stillborn. She had been pregnant five times and had no living children. This last pregnancy looked hopeful. She had made it to her seventh month, then suddenly, rapidly delivered.

"OB is a happy place to work. We just don't know how to handle this."

Sighing, I walked the long corridor to her room at the end of the hall. She was sitting at the head of the bed with her legs pulled up, resting her chin on her knees. The curtain was pulled three quarters of the way, so I pulled it the rest of the way and sat down. "Elizabeth, my name is Joy, and I'm here to help about the baby." She started weeping and so did I. We just sat there holding each other, sobbing. In came a gynecology nurse who said, "Well, I was going to talk to you about care, you know, your vagina. Now spray your vagina with this three times a day, and wash your hands." I said, "Just a second. Either sit down and bawl with us or get out."

"Did you see your baby, Elizabeth?" When she said, "No." I said, "Would you like to?"

"Oh, yes."

I said, "I'll tell you what, I'll just run down and bring her right up here. And we'll be with her, if you would like that."

But she said, "No," and I thought I don't want to force her. "I have to go where she is." Which was the morgue—not a very nice place in the bowels of the institution.

"Okay, Elizabeth, let me check first. I'll be right back."

I ran down the steps and into the pathology office. I experienced some difficulty forcing myself to enter the morgue proper. It had only been a week since I had accidentally locked myself in those cool confines.

There was a body there—an adult male with a tag on his toe.

And then on another litter a little blue blanket in a bundle. I went over and opened it. She was beautiful, just perfect, but extremely tiny — her little face was perfect. I went over to turn her over and she had a post mortem examination. The whole back of her head had been opened, and her brain examined. So I wrapped her up and went back to Elizabeth.

"Now Elizabeth, I want to tell you this. Do you remember last night signing that it was okay for a post mortem on your little girl?" She said yes, and I said, "Well, that operation has been done, but her face is fine. I wanted you to know that there are some incisions on her little body where they examined her, just in case you changed your mind about seeing her."

"I'm ready, get the wheel chair."

She was going to go home that day, so I said, "What about your husband? We could wait for him. He's coming to take you home, and there is no problem about discharge by eleven."

"No, I need to do this alone."

I said okay and put her in a wheelchair. Beautiful and stately, she was still sobbing. We got on the elevator, and I told the operator, "one, please." The elevator operator is used to people being discharged this time of day, so he said, "She going home, huh?"

"No, she's not going home."

"What's the matter with her?"

"Nothing, just leave her alone."

We got down there, and it's a circuitous route into the bowels of the institution. I went back in the refrigerator again, and got the little bundle. We went into the pathologist's office, which was air-conditioned (it was summer) and had a carpet and a comfortable chair and lamp. A lot softer environment than the morgue.

"Would you like to be alone?" I asked, wanting to give her that dignity.

"No, would you please stay?"

"Of course." I handed her the baby, and in the process, the limp little body had twisted in the blanket, so it was the back of the baby's head that she saw first.

I said, "I'm really sorry, Elizabeth, let me fix her."

I rewrapped the infant, tucking her beautiful little face in the blanket, and gave her back to her mother. Then I stood back. She started rocking and crooning.

I said, "What is her name?"

"Jessica." Then she started talking to her, not to me. She said, "Oh, do you remember how I would walk and carry you in me and I would show you trees and tell you that you would be swinging in trees and climbing trees and that trees were your friends and about the birds. And do you remember the music I would play for you?"

After about ten minutes, she said, "I'm finished now, thank you." I took her back up to her room and asked if she would like to be alone.

"Yes, please."

I left and hurried to call her husband, a lawyer, who had already left his office to come and get her. I ran around the nurses' station and tried to borrow money from a couple of interns who didn't have any. Then I grabbed an oncologist, who gave me a twenty. I ran down to the florist shop and got her a dozen red roses because a mother should never leave the hospital without something in her arms.

I intercepted Elizabeth's husband as he walked out of the elevator. Handing him the roses I explained how a dear friend who had lost her newborn to death taught me about grief in motherhood.

His eyes filled with tears and his voice broke as he said thank you.

After helping Elizabeth into their car and waving a shakey goodby I felt my sadness mixed with a little pride. I knew I helped, through sensitivity and genuine concern. I assumed nothing. I did it right for her because I gave her control over her situation ... tragic as it was. I asked her what she wanted to do then acknowledged her wisdom by complying with her request. Death was her enemy but I was her servant. She was the teacher, now, and I was honored to be the student.

Elizabeth left me with the profound lesson of never saying to a patient "I know what you're going through." This statement has been referred to as the empathetic lie. Unless you have actually experienced a similar loss you cannot possibly know how the other person is feeling.

Lastly, even if you did lose a stillborn infant you still cannot fully comprehend the depth of this particular loss to this particular patient.

Acknowledge that you can't imagine her pain but that you're willing to hear her put into words some of the hurt she's feeling.

This is another way to give her roses.

WHAT DO YOU WANT NOW?

ONE DAY I WAS ASKED TO SEE A YOUNG 42 YEAR OLD WOMAN who had cancer of the trachea. (She got that way by smoking two packs of cigarettes a day for fourteen years.) Chemotherapy had been totally unsuccessful. Radiation therapy had resulted only in burning and scarring the remaining healthy trachea tissue.

On entering her hospital room, I quickly assumed her status: terminal and losing ground rapidly. I knew better than to waste time with social amenities.

"Shirley, my name is Joy. What do you want now?"

"I want Tom to be able to visit me anytime," she whispered hoarsely.

"Consider it done."

Her request was a simple one and easily granted. I went to the main information desk and told the Gray Lady with Blue Hair to make a note on the roladex that Mr. Long was permitted to visit his wife unrestrictedly.

Several days later, a Saturday, I was called from my garden by the nurse caring for Shirley. It seems earlier that day, Tom had been in an automobile accident and demolished his car. Over the phone, Shirley's nurse had told me that Tom was injured seriously enough to require hospitalization, and that Shirley was hysterical. Would I hurry?

I jumped in my truck, and drove quickly to the hospital. Clad in Wrangler jeans and a Mickey Mouse t-shirt, I ran to Shirley's room. The hospital was filled to over-flowing. Instead of her being on a medical-surgical unit, Shirley had been admitted to the Gynecology floor. She was sitting up in bed, gasping for air. The tumor had almost completely obstructed her trachea. In a panic over Tom's condition she was hyperventilating. Eyes bulging and hands yanking at the covers, she was close to hysteria.

Without many words, I swung her out of bed, into a wheelchair, grabbed a portable tank of oxygen, and entered the elevator for a quick trip three flights up. I wheeled her directly into Tom's room, where he lay suffering from multiple cuts, abrasions, and possible internal injuries. He certainly looked damaged but not dying. Shirley talked briefly with Tom. Then, reassured, she began to settle down and require much less oxygen. Aften five or ten minutes, convinced that Tom would survive, she asked me to take her back to her room. I gave her an injection for sleep and a goodnight kiss.

Monday, I found Tom to be even more sore and aching but in no danger. By Wednesday, he had even attempted to hobble down the steps to visit with Shirley. Many nurses had been giving verbal and non-verbal communication that they were entirely too busy to find a wheelchair, wait for an elevator, take Tom to visit, wait, then take him back to his room.

While visiting Shirley, I watched her roommate who had been hospitalized for a D & C packing to go home.

Suddenly, I had a brilliant idea! "Shirley, I've got another roommate for you, if you want him."

"Oh, Joy, could you do that?", she whispered.

"Sure, nothing to it. Let me just run up and talk with Tom about it."

Sitting on the side of his bed, I provided him with all the information I could so he was able to make the best decision for him. "She's quite ill, Tom. In fact, she's slipping from us. I wonder how you'd feel about being in the room if she'd die?"

"Oh, gosh, it is to that point?"

"Yes, she's very bad. I just want to be straight with you."

"See, I was going to take her home, you know, before this accident and all. Oh, Hell, let's do it!"

"Okay, Tom, get your shaving kit and stuff ready, and I'll be right back. I just want to check with the Gynecology supervisor."

Sitting in her office, she tried to appear cool. Instead, she was betrayed by her words. "Absolutely not, Miss Ufema, and don't do this!"

"Could we please discuss this?"

"There's nothing to discuss. He shouldn't be in that room with her."

I always shudder a little when I hear people use the word 'should'. It seems to denote an air of superiority and exclusiveness about the only way life is to be lived.

"Well, she's quite ill, you know. She could go out."

"I am fully aware of her condition — that she may die soon, and so is her husband. I still don't understand your resistance."

"I've got it now. Here's why they shouldn't be in the same room ... This is a gynecology floor."

"Right. Go on."

Mr. Long is a male."

"Go on."

Well, males stand up to pee."

"True."

"That could disrupt the entire gynecology services!"

With that kind of logic, I had no alternative. I ran up three flights of steps, snitched Tom and his shaving kit, gently plunked him down into a wheelchair, and took him to Shirley. After closing their door, I went to the nurses' station to write a new care-plan. However, the fur flew! Six threatened women began to chastise and prattle until I reminded them, "Dying is simply taking turns. Shirley is having her turn just a bit earlier than any of us, but she certainly has the right to expect one of us, who profess to be caregivers, to help her do this her way."

I returned the following morning to find Tom and Shirley sitting on the same bed. She had eaten a little breakfast and, for the first time in two weeks, it stayed down. She slept from 7:30 that evening through twelve hours till 7:30 the next morning without any medication for sleep or for pain.

I can still feel her hug and hear her whisper from that rotting trachea, "Thanks a lot, Joy."

The important point I want to emphasize here is that by giving human beings, especially those approaching death, the dignity of making their own decisions, we are giving all there is to give.

In Shirley's case, the physicians and specialists were in agreement that nothing more could be done for her. Not true! Our work was just beginning. It just changes form, and we may not recognize it until it's too late. It's very simple. Just ask your patient, not his physician, or his spouse, or his social worker; ask your patient, "what do you want now?" (Now that your condition is worse than it was three weeks ago). "From *whom* do you want it?" (Very important. The patient may prefer someone else to talk with than you. Don't take it personally as I used to. Just because you've studied Death and Dying for six years doesn't mean you're the best helper for this particular patient. Lastly, find out when the patient wants what he wants. He may need you to track down his sister in Philadelphia by next Wednesday because that day is his birthday.

By utilizing these three universal questions, specifically from the patient, you can always be sure you're doing what is best for the individual. Without a rulebook it's too easy in this kind of nebulous work to get caught up in exploiting the dying patient or taking advantage of his vulnerability. If you enter his room and talk at him, he can't get up and leave; and he probably won't ask you to. Constantly ask yourself — "Is this for me or for him?" If you remember these questions, it will always be for him.

CARRIE

I MIGHT AS WELL HONESTLY ADMIT THAT I WAS AFRAID TO WORK with dying children. While attending numerous conferences I would always choose an afternoon workshop geared to the special needs of the terminally ill child. I also read a lot on the subject and felt safe in an academic way, but I just couldn't seem to place myself in an actual experience. I finally had to sit down and ask my favorite question: "What is the worst thing that could happen?"

"Well, I might cry in front of the child."

"Yes, but if that happens the kid will at least know you care."

"True, but maybe my crying will tell him he's dying."

"He already knows."

"Right."

"Studies show, and the literature seems to support, that children as young as eighteen months know."

"Right."

"In working with children we all tend to assume the little kid is upset because he's seriously ill and therefore will never get to go to the junior prom or experience college and a first job. But "children" don't work that way. "They're more pragmatic. They worry more over a dirty diaper, what time Mom will be in to visit, and whether or not they have to have a bone marrow tap tomorrow."

The self-discussion helped. The next day I introduced myself to Carrie. She was three years old and had leukemia.

Every day, for two weeks, I'd play with her. I'd just climb into her crib and we'd color together.

We'd eat pretzels and drink ginger ale. It took a long time to build a relationship with her. For a very long while she never shared any of her feelings with me.

We were coloring one day when out of the blue, she said, "I had a mouse once but it died." I said, "How did you know it was dead?"

"Well, it didn't move."

I said, "Yeah, that's how it is when you're dead." Then I asked her what she did with it.

"Oh, we buried it in the ground."

"Then what will happen to the mouse?"

"Nothing. It will just stay in the ground." Then she said, "Or it might come up in the spring as a flower." It was just such sweet innocence. I asked if she would draw me some pictures, and she said yes.

I asked her to draw me something that would really make her happy. She drew me, smiling, with my nurse's hat on. I took my hat off and gave it to her.

Proud of my earthshaking conversation, I hastened to record every detail. Sitting at the end of the nurses' station, I was struck in the elbow by a metal chart shoved across the desk. It was tossed by Carrie's oncologist, who said curtly, "This isn't anything new. I don't find anything profound in her words." I felt sorry for him. Obviously, he was angry because her peripheral blood smear revealed 92% blasts instead of 0% blasts. He allowed his anger to prevent him from sitting down and getting to know her, and he resented anyone else doing it.

Later that week Carrie was discharged from the hospital and went home to be cared for by her young parents.

About three weeks later, on the desk in my office, I found my cap and a note from Carrie's mother saying she had died at home.

True, nothing profound. Just a very brave little girl leaving life. I hope she comes up in the spring, as a flower.

7

SURE, IT'S FUNNY, NOW!

" I WONDER IF KUBLER-ROSS STARTED OUT THIS WAY," I said out loud to four cold walls and two, just-as-cold corpses. It was either fifteen minutes or two weeks that I had been accidentally locked in the morgue.

The whole thing certainly began innocently. I was companioning a young woman at her death bed. Her family also was keeping watch and we all felt exhausted hours later when the end finally came. She died around seven o'clock during the evening shift, which was, as usual, short-staffed. After I promised to personally attend to her post-mortem care, her husband and sons were eager to leave. She had suffered over a year with cancer of the pancreas and was merely skin and bones.

With ease, I lifted her freshly-washed frail body onto the litter and proceeded to the basement of the hospital. Usually an orderly accompanies nursing staff to assist in transferring the body to the morgue table. Earlier, I had declined an offer from Big John for help. The p.m. care was hectic, and he still had three male patients to shave before hernia surgery.

"Besides, John, she's very light in weight. I can handle her alone. Thanks, anyway."

The freight elevator moaned and creaked as it lowered me into the bowels of the institution. With a jerk, it stopped and opened its gaping doors to allow me to step directly into the morgue. With surprising quickness, the doors closed behind me, leaving me and my companion alone in a dimly lit foyer. I fumbled in my pocket for the key, fetched earlier from the emergency room, and deftly maneuvered the litter into the large refrigerator. Another body lay in state with a name tag tied to a big toe.

Engrossed in lifting my patient onto the morgue table, I pulled my foot away from the door, allowing it to silently swing shut. The transfer required some wrestling of dead weight. My task completed with respect and dignity, I adjusted the sheet one more time to cover her face. Innocently, I moved towards the door, pulling the litter behind. It was then that my attention was drawn to the handle of this solid oak door. The lock to it was on the outside, and so were my keys I suppose swinging merrily.

I'm not a genius. I learn with average speed and feel I grasp information quickly enough. However, the message of this particular situation did not register for several minutes. I suppose it was due to the absurdity of it all, or perhaps that, deep down, I knew my two roommates would not offer much in the way of conversation until 9 o'clock the next morning when the pathologist arrived. Ah ha! Yes! That's right! The pathologist. I knew his office was adjacent to the morgue, so I turned around and sure enough, another door. If I could just get to his phone and page Eugene, all would be well. With great calm, I approached the door, placed my hand on the knob, and turned. Nothing. Obviously locked. At the far end of the refrigerator was another door. Perhaps it led to somewhere, anywhere. Well, not *anywhere!*

Stepping past the two bodies, I anxiously approached the door. With trepidation, I reached for the shiny knob, held fast for a moment, then turned. It moved! At last. I quickly pulled the door open, eager to be released from my chilling prison. Fate was not kind. I was staring into a closet with several mops and buckets scattered over the tile floor. Not even a magazine. (At this point, I would have been elated to find even a phone book.)

I closed the betraying door and turned to look for a place to sit. I became increasingly aware of the chill. Outside of the hospital, it was a hot August evening with people seeking relief from the humidity. I'd be happy to invite six or seven folks in to share my cool retreat. We could even play bridge. We could have two dummy hands. Oh, no. My humor was turning macabre.

It was at this point that I began to whistle. I think I whistled, "Whistle a Happy Tune." It was a voluntary act, and I was totally aware of its genesis. Something else realized was a feeling totally involuntary. Some of you *quick* readers are probably way ahead of me. I had an unrelenting urge to urinate. In spite of the fact that I had worked for a year on the Urology floor and even had earned the coveted yellow shoes award, I could not then, or even now, explain why the peeing sensation accompanies stress. Well now, we do have a problem because we all know when yougotta-goyougottago! I was examining a drain in the floor when suddenly the morgue door slowly opened and my eyes fell upon a pair of white trousers. I glanced upward into the questioning stare of Big John's marvelous black face.

"What are you doing there?" he said.

"Wha, ah, I, ah, think I dropped a quarter down this drain."

"Well, here, I'll help ya take the top out," he magnanamously offered.

"Na, let it go. Let's go, I ah, gotta get going. Thanks anyway, John."

"Say, listen," he said, "how long were you down here? I went to the ER to get the key 'cause some dude up on M-10 croaked, you know, and they said it was still signed out under your name."

"Yes, well, I, ah, was just finishing up and all. By the way, did you get the key?"

"Yeah, right where you left it."

"I see. This could just be our little secret, right?"

"Right," he smiled, walking away whistling.

A close friend is the Head Nurse of a 16-bed unit exclusively designated for patients with chronic obstructive pulmonary diseases. This work is terribly depressing. All of the patients have faulty lungs and spend years of their shortened lives gasping for breath. Their deaths are painful, drawn-out, frightening events.

Occasionally, however, a bit of humor manages to evade the Grim Reaper and serve to remind us that maybe death isn't all that bad, and for that matter, neither is life.

During a particularly hectic afternoon Harry was admitted to the pulmonary unit. Like most patients, he was biting the air for oxygen. His face was ashen and his fingernails blue. He was obviously frightened. Between gasps, chokes, and coughing Harry let it be known to the entire nursing staff that he, and he alone, was in charge of his own destiny. Not unlike many of the other patients in the unit, he was attempting to take some control over the uncontrollable remainder of his life. However, there was one difference between Harry and those other patients. He reigned from his bed-throne with a hat firmly fixed upon his head. During numerous admission procedures such as blood removal from a large artery in his groin, to breathing treatments and exercises Harry managed to retain his hat. Certainly it was the epitome of control. (I've seen the reverse behavior manifested by mildly rebellious nurses who *refuse* to wear their hats!)

The staff of breathing experts appeared oblivious to Harry's hat. Working with a quiet efficiency, they attached tubes to take oxygen in and tubes to take urine out. Blood was removed and blood was transfused. Sputum was suctioned from his lungs and pills were popped down his throat. The team was losing and they knew it. No one was able to pull a rabbit out of the hat. Harry seemed to sense it too because he increased his cussing, and from the depth of his soul, struggled to sit up and, in a surprisingly loud voice said, "God damn it! Help me get my breath!" and collapsing, hat falling off, he died.

This event was so unexpected that the nurses and doctors standing around the bed were speechless. The suction machine continued humming as if to remind those still participating in life that life does go on, and on.

After several very long minutes, one of the respiratory therapists gingerly retrieved Harry's hat from among the sheets and reverently set it upon the dead man's head.

It was at this exact moment that several team members looked at each other, measuring what behavior might be the most appropriate.

Very slowly, subtly, but insistently, the giggle began. Infectiously, it spread, unrelentingly from one person to the next.

Within seconds, the bed was shaking from seven tired, but very human beings, muffling great belly laughs at Harry's hat.

'The chortle broke into laughter. There was no stopping it, and I'm glad. Over the five years this unit was open for business there had been hundreds of deaths. The laughter and chuckles were not disrespectful to Harry. It was actually a funny sight, so why not laugh?

About twenty minutes later, after Harry's body was washed and wrapped in a clean sheet, two orderlies came to take him to the morgue.

There were more muffled giggles as Harry laid out on a litter, his hat on his head, was majestically rolled down the corridor.

There is a favorite joke among nurses regarding a physician who died and went to Heaven. Saint Peter conducted a tour of the place and at noon suggested he and the physician break for lunch. At the cafeteria a long line had assembled. In a rather rude manner, the doctor pushed in front of people, picked up his tray and silverware then proceeded to bully his way up to the front of the line.

Saint Peter scurried after him and escorted him back. "Hey, look here, Doctor," admonished the Keeper of the Gate, "you can't act like that! Up here, everyone is equal."

Chided, the doctor stood quietly in line, sulking.

Suddenly, there arrived a man with a long beard, wearing sandals and a flowing white robe. Around his neck was a stethoscope.

He pushed his way in between people, picked up his tray and silverware then busted his way in front of everyone and marched to the front of the line.

Appalled, the doctor grabbed Saint Peter by the arm and tattled, "Hey, did you see that? I thought you said everyone up here was equal! Who *was* that?"

"Oh, yes, that was God, and sometimes he likes to play Doctor."

I was sitting beside Mr. Cook's death bed. For several months I had spent long hours giving him nursing care for his cancer of the stomach. Occasionally we would share a few words about his favorite subject — antique cars. Mostly it was a quiet time, holding hands, speaking softly, and supporting his wife. Suddenly the solitude was interrupted by Mr. Cook's physician charging into the room and shouting at me to get out! He grabbed me by the arm and "assisted" me out the door. "Get out and stay out!"

Enraged, I headed for my boss's office. While examining the situation and waiting for her administrative action, the phone rang. The surgeon was calling and offering an apology.

I returned to Mr. Cook's room where his wife was discussing assertively with the surgeon my value to her husband. "Carl has received much comfort from Joy's visits. We both want her here."

"I guess I've got egg on my face," he said to me. "It's all right, you may stay."

"Well, thank you, Doctor, but what about all your other terminal patients? May I see them too?"

"Call me first."

"I will."

I did. He said okay, every time.

One patient said, "If I could live my life over again I wouldn't take life so seriously. Learn to laugh more, Joy."

I guess a lesson in life that has been the most valuable to me is knowing I have the freedom to choose how I wish to respond to any situation. If I'm caught in heavy traffic on my way to a dentist appointment I can choose to grin and bear it or fuss and fume, honk the horn, cuss, and elevate my blood pressure. All of which does nothing towards the removal of the stalled vehicle on the South bridge.

The following story will demonstrate the effectiveness of laughing at a situation, where no one was hurt.

I was attending my second funeral in as many days. Today would be different. Today I would stay close in line as we drove to the cemetery so no fool could swerve from his lane into the middle of a long funeral cortege.

Yesterday, as I was leaving the mortuary to get in my car to join the procession, I was approached by the funeral director.

"Joy, the family is very grateful for all the help you provided so

Mrs. Bailey has requested you stand with her at the graveside for the twenty-one gun military salute.''

"Of course, Bob, I'd be honored."

We all drove off, with our lights on, accompanied by a police escort. This particular officer was quite adept at maneuvering his motorcycle in and around traffic to maintain a steady procession of mourners. But, he pulled up at an intersection quite far ahead of the main group, then neglected to wait until his entire flock was safely through.

Suddenly, from another lane, a young chap pulled his blue and silver Camaro directly in front of me then stopped, obediently at a notoriously long red light.

Trapped, I watched helplessly as the hearse, family car, and half the cortege drove on to their destination. It suddenly became apparent to me that I did not know the location of the burial. In my grief, which was not overwhelming, just saddening, I had forgotten to inquire from Bob, the merry mortician, in which cemetery Mr. Bailey was to be buried.

Jumping from my truck I ran up to the Camaro and tapped roughly on the window. Inside sat a fellow in his twenties, eyes closed, head swaying, fingers, functioning as quasi drumsticks, beating to a tune I was unable to hear. Startled, he rolled down the window about one half of an inch.

"Hey, yeh, man, like, ah, what's up?"

"You stupid poophead," I shouted above the blasting radio, "You're in the middle of a funeral procession and now we're stuck at this stop light!"

"Hey, yeh, man, funeral you say, oh, wow — groovy."

Blaring horns from others waiting in line told me the light was green. Behind my truck sat twelve vehicles, headlights announcing to traffic that they were mourners, all dressed in black with no place to go.

I drove off quickly with the others close behind. Unfortunately we were delayed several times by traffic and signal lights.

During one of these rest stops I ran to the car behind me and inquired if they knew the name of the cemetery. No, they were from Illinois (*distantly* related to the deceased).

By the time I reached the fourth car, the driver had antici-
pated my visit and was leaning out the window waving one of
those little cards with a picture of the Praying Hands upon it, and
information regarding date of birth and death and "site of
interment."

"It's at the Moravian Cemetery in Lititz, wherever that is."

"Great, I know how to get to Lititz, maybe we can catch up
with them. Stay with me, I'm gonna go fast."

Although it was a two-lane highway, we made good time and
arrived at the entrance to the cemetery. I heard the unmistak-
able sound of a twenty-one gun salute.

We ran across the grass to the canopy just as people were filing
back to their cars.

I spotted the funeral director pacing nervously by the casket.
"Bob."

"Where *were* you? You were supposed to be standing with the
widow!" he whispered hoarsely.

"Some fool cut in the procession way back on Marshall Ave-
nue. Listen, for future reference, have the police make sure
everybody gets through all the lights, will you?"

"Yeah, sure. You really should have been here. Don't tell Mrs.
Bailey you missed the whole thing."

I don't know why I was taken back by his ridiculous statement.

Undertakers are frequently attempting to conceal the truth
from all of us.

Did he actually think Mrs. Bailey would not know I wasn't
standing beside her?

Because I developed an open, honest relationship with the
Bailey family through the process I felt a responsibility to continue on that level.

Hugging Mrs. Bailey I said quietly, "I'm sorry I'm late, some
damn fool drove in the middle of the procession and I got lost."

Smiling she looked up at me and said, "It's all right. You were
always with us when we desperately needed you. I don't think
Mr. Bailey will hold a grudge."

IF I SHOULD DIE BEFORE I LIVE

8

H E WAS ONLY 46 YEARS OLD WITH A YOUNG WIFE, THREE daughters and a son. His cancer began in the thyroid gland and hadn't caused too much trouble for about one year. Unknown to his physician, the damn stuff was silently spreading into his spinal cord. He was admitted to the hospital. His presenting symptom was lower limb paralysis. He would remain in bed until his death, two years later. During that time, I became quite close to him and his family. Born in Italy, he came to the United States when he was 21 and worked for the railroad. It was an excellent job, affording him frequent visits to his homeland. After one such tour, he returned to America with a dark-haired beauty named Marie. Four babies later she would come to the hospital to attend to her husband.

Michael was a nice enough fellow, but he was from the old country and a bit difficult. He ordered me and the other nurses around and expected silent obedience to his whims.

I was sure his behavior stemmed from an attempt to control. Since he was a prisoner to his bed he had lost much of the control over his life that most of us take for granted.

I can't imagine how difficult it must have been for him.

Some days he was quite pleasant, actually bargaining out loud with the saints. On other days he would be mean and miserable, displacing and projecting. Nothing suited him.

"Here, Joy, fix this pillow again, and get it right this time!"

"Michael," I said gently, "just relax and tell me nicely when you're uncomfortable."

"I'm always uncomfortable! What would you know about being in bed for a year, paralyzed?"

He turned his head to face the wall.

I pulled a chair close to his bed and sat down. As tough and gruff as he could sometimes be I sensed a grieving in him that he rarely expressed openly.

With great difficulty I kept quiet. I reached for his hand and he allowed me to hold it. I waited for him to speak, knowing that the words he would choose at this unique moment might be illuminating.

Many silent minutes later he said, "I never should have done it."

"Done what?" I inquired.

"Brought Marie here."

"*Here,* to the hospital?" seeking clarification.

"No! America! I should never have brought her to America. Now I'm not going to be around to take care of her and our children."

There were no tears. He was just being pragmatic.

Suddenly he pulled his hand from mine and said in a tough voice, "I don't wanna talk no more about this. Nurse, get me some juice. I need some juice."

"I'm happy to get your juice, Michael, but I want to tell you that I care very much about you and your family and anytime you want to share your feelings with me I'm available."

Our eyes met, briefly; then,

"Get me some juice, now."

For many weeks I accompanied him in the ambulance as we rode from Harrisburg Hospital to Polyclinic Hospital for his daily cobalt treatments.

Although the journey lasted half an hour both ways he rarely entered into any conversation with me and answered my questions curtly.

One morning around nine o'clock I was walking down the hall to his room when I heard shouting.

A student nurse scurried from his room muttering,

"I can't take it, anymore. I should have been an airline stewardess instead of a nurse."

Entering the room I found Michael jibbering in Italian then shouting in English. Finally, I got him quieted down enough to provide me with an explanation.

"I've been waiting over three months for Saint Patrick's Cathedral here in town to get me Holy Water from Lourdes. They have it now and Marie, she not here yet!"

"I know your wife doesn't drive, Michael, would you like me to go get her?"

His face lit up. I wasn't sure exactly why my offer would be received with such exuberance when I suddenly realized he was looking past me at the doorway. I turned to see, Marie carrying a small, precious vial. I gave her a hug and returned to my office.

A bit later the phone rang. It was the return call from Dr. Groff, Michael's radiologist.

"Thanks for calling back, Leonard, I was wondering what the status might be on our mutual patient."

"No so hot, Joy, in fact I'm discontinuing cobalt treatments. He has extensive tumor involvement into his lumbar vertebra and I'm afraid the spinal cord is permanently damaged. I'm sorry as Hell."

"Thanks, Doctor, so am I."

Michael was informed of his condition and prognosis. Since nothing more could be done, he was discharged over the weekend. I visited three or four times a month for close to a year. He was always the same. He never read a newspaper or a book. He rarely watched television. He would lie in bed, receive visitors, issue orders to his wife and children and constantly pray for a miracle. His life was consumed by the forthcoming miracle.

Marie and I share December 17th as a mutual birthday. She had invited me for my favorite spaghetti dinner. This particular evening found me in good spirits, and I accepted a third glass of rich, red wine. As I helped with washing the dishes my glass remained full despite the frequent sipping I performed. Giggles from the children told me they had been refilling my glass each time I turned my back.

Feeling a bit courageous, I pulled a chair up to Michael's bedside.

"Want a little company?" I asked.

"Sure, you know I always like it when you visit."

"I'm not sure I care to visit again," I said, then held my breath.

"Why not? You don't like my family?" he asked, incredulously.

"I love your family, Michael, and this birthday dinner was very special."

"Why then? What is the worry?"

"It's you."

"Me? I don't cause no problem. I don't do nothing."

"That's just it, Michael. You don't do anything. For eighteen months . . ."

"Nineteen!" he interrupted.

"OK, for nineteen months you've lain here. I can't imagine how difficult it must be, but . . ."

"It's damned difficult!" he interrupted again.

"I'm sure it is, but you've wasted close to two years of your life and you could waste how many more?"

"What *can* I do? I'm paralyzed!"

"Michael, you can be more appreciative. Don't order Marie around. Can't you ask nicely? Can't you even thank her sometimes? (The wine was stirring around). The kids are afraid of you, and you've never sat Frankie down and talked to him about what it means to be an Italian male. You've never given him a part of your heart, let alone your watch or penknife. I'm telling you this because my father worked for the railroad, too. He died suddenly one day in the middle of the machine shop. We didn't have time to talk about life and death. You do. Take advantage of it, please before it's too late."

"I'm waiting for a miracle. God is going to give me a miracle," he said, quietly, staring at the crucifix hanging on the wall.

I stood up, a bit shaky, but I spoke clearly. Placing my hand on his arm, I said, "Michael, God already gave you the miracle. You're in your own home, being cared for by a loving family. Why don't you simply enjoy this miracle, there might not be another."

He said nothing.

I kissed his cheek and left.

The next time I was to see him was for his final admission into the hospital, where, three weeks later, he died.

His son is a young man now. I see him periodically at public functions. Somehow I just don't think it appropriate to ask if he ever had that special chat with his Dad.

I think it's important here to point out that we don't have to be victims, either to the people we love or to life.

Everyday, everywhere events happen to us that are not of our choosing.

Perhaps our boss reprimands us late Friday afternoon. We're upset from the encounter. Angered, we usually say,

"Darn, now he ruined my whole weekend by telling me I'm not working fast enough. What a lousy thing to do to me."

In reality, no one has the power to ruin our weekend. We *choose* to respond to the situation by selecting upset and angry as our response.

We could have just as easily chosen not to be upset or angry. We do have that power.

We could say,

"Nothing is going to ruin my weekend. I might consider what the boss said and explore honestly if he might have been accurate. Either way, right or wrong in his analysis, I'll deal with it Monday."

We have total control over our attitudes, even though we may have little control over the behavior of others.

DON'T SECOND-GUESS ME

A S A CHILD, THEN YOUNG-ADULT, I HAD NEVER BEEN PARTICU-
larly close to Uncle Win. My father's brother, a bachelor
and gifted artist, lived reclusively in the old homestead.
Over the past years, especially since my father died, I developed
an interest in my heritage. During occasional visits to Altoona I
would enjoy chatting about events prior to my birth. Uncle Win
took delight in these recalls of memories and frequently would
bless me with a trinket or two from my long-departed grandparents. I began assembling old photographs, ancient books and
letters, and a few kitchen utensils brought from England. I even
transplanted, to my own yard, day lillies and grapes from the
80-year old homestead.

During my annual visit at Christmas I walked up the winding,
run down, puddle filled driveway to visit Uncle Win. He was
quite idiosyncratic, the artistic temperament I supposed, so I was
never quite sure how he would react to my visits, or anyone's
visit, especially during emotional-filled holidays. However, I was
totally unprepared for what greeted me.

Several minutes passed as I waited at the back door after
knocking loudly. Still no answer. The 1956 Nash Rambler sat in
the barn. He had to be home. Peering in through the dirty
window in the kitchen I couldn't believe my eyes. He was shuf-
fling weakly to the door, barely able to walk. With great difficulty he released the lock then stood back, leaning against the
cupboard. I entered and was immediately hit by the smell. Every
nurse can identify it—bloody stool. My usual memory of that

kitchen was an odor of tobacco and woodstove. The smell of blood forced me to look at him, though I didn't want to. The family was dying out, and although we never shared a deep relationship, I did love him and my eyes did not want to confirm what I already knew.

He was dying.

He stood by the cupboard with the beautiful stencilwork he himself had done. Although swathed in sweaters, he shivered — obviously anemic from loss of blood. His face was gray and waxen. I could barely distinguish his lips. Upon his head sat a too-small blue, cotton cap. His hands were covered with brown jersey gloves. Baggy trousers, dirtied with incontinent, bloody bowel movement. He wore my grandfather's old slippers, sides split from his swollen feet and ankles — liver involvement with tumor.

I was embarrassed for both of us.

"Come on, Uncle Win, let me help you in to the couch."

Together, we staggered drunkenly into the first living room. A blood-splattered trail wove from the kitchen through the dining room and ended at a makeshift potty at the foot of the stairs.

He fell-sat onto the sofa, short of breath and groaning as he clutched his right side.

I placed the ridiculous Christmas gift of Hickory Farms cheeses and meats unobtrusively on the piano bench, then gently sat beside him.

"What do you think?" he whispered.

Hesitantly, I said, "I think we're in trouble, Uncle Win."

"Yeah, I thought so."

"You know, Uncle Win, I understand how much your life-style means to you; especially in this neat, old house and all, but things are seriously different now, and I don't want to assume anything or second-guess you at all."

He nodded.

"I think you're sicker now than you ever have been in your whole life, so maybe you might want something different than you usually have."

"I don't know what you mean."

"I mean, you've always preferred living alone, but now, maybe you want something else."

"Like what?" he glared at me.

"Well, like maybe you would like me to stay here with you or perhaps you might prefer going to the hospital. Or, you could even come to my home and I'd take care of you there."

"Make the arrangements."

"For what, Uncle Win?"

"For the hospital," he gasped.

Two hundred miles away I tried for several days to telephone his physician. After finally making contact, I learned of the extensiveness of his disease. Cancer of the bowel, liver, lung, and bones. He couldn't last a week and didn't.

I phoned him long distance.

"Uncle Win, this is Joy. How are you feeling?"

"Much better. The pneumonia in my lungs has improved and everything is going to be all right."

"Uncle Win, I know that everything is not going to be all right."

"How do you know that?" he snapped.

"Because I just talked with Dr. Statler."

Silence.

"I want to know, from you, Uncle Win, what you want now."

"Well, I don't want to talk about it. That's what I want."

"OK, but I want you to know that if you do want to talk, anytime, I'm happy to listen."

"I won't ever want to."

"That's OK, Uncle Win. I also want you to know, since I never told you this before, that I love you."

Silence.

He died five days later.

A valuable point I want to reemphasize is never to assume or second-guess. I've learned we die the way we live. (We are consistent in our coping mechanisms, that is.) Our pattern of behavior in past crisis is usually consistent with how we deal with the biggest crisis we'll ever face — our dying.

Just because my uncle was reticently victorian in his life style, however, does not necessarily box him into being that way with his death style. I felt it important enough to at least offer him an alternative, an opportunity to share with me or anyone, his feelings about having to die.

I might have predicted accurately his response and we see through the telephone conversation that I was correct. At least I did not have to stand before his casket and berate myself, adding guilt to my grief, that I was positive he wouldn't want to talk.

Or would he? Now it's too late. I'm a bit saddened that he didn't share with me because I loved him but at least I was couragous enough to ask.

Florence was a terribly strong woman emotionally. Her son-in-law, a dentist, discovered a fast-growing tumor on the floor of her mouth. Within months, the damned thing had destroyed her entire lower jaw. She suffered for over a year with it, then began losing weight rapidly when she could no longer swallow liquids. An option was proposed to her regarding an incision through the skin and a tube inserted directly into her stomach for feedings. She refused.

She was devoutly religious, and more than ready to pass on. However, her grotesque physical appearance bothered her tremendously. The nurses were quite skilled at dressing her face with bandages, but still she shrank away in her room.

In December of 1980, I was contacted at the Hospice office in Lancaster, Pennsylvania, by a reporter for *People Magazine.* They were interested in writing an article about my work with terminally ill persons.

When the photographer asked to take pictures of some of my favorite patients, I immediately thought of Florence. I admired her stoicism and she had a special place in my heart, but I was certain she would never comply with the request for photographs. I do, however, firmly believe in never second-guessing

I made a special visit to the hospital, knocked on her door, and entered. She was seated high on the bed, resting against many pillows.

"Florence, we've talked seriously on many occasions, and I feel like I know you quite well. Instead of me making a decision for you, I just want to present my idea and allow you to decide for yourself."

"Well," she mumbled, "I think you know me pretty good, too. What are you going to ask?"

"A favor. *People Magazine* is doing an article about my work with dying persons, and they would like some pictures. Even though I'm aware of your feelings about your face, I would never second-guess your feelings about having your picture taken for a magazine. So I'm just asking you what you would like to do."

"I've seen that magazine. I wouldn't mind at all," she answered enthusiastically.

"You wouldn't? Thank you, Florence."

"Thank you, and thanks for not just assuming."

It turned out that having her picture appear in *People Magazine* was the only claim to fame Florence ever experienced. It didn't matter that her head and jaw were bandaged. It was her legacy. Her smile shone through.

While working with dying patients I find it useful to assist them in sorting out what was outstanding, to them, about their life. Almost everyone finds solace, in their final days and weeks, in reviewing their life, non-judgmentally, accentuating what, for them, were positive contributions. This may be a difficult task, especially for the depressed patient but it can be done through gentleness and sensitivity.

Margaret was the mother of nineteen children. She was suffering a bit longer than any of us had wanted. The malignancy in her bowel had spread throughout her pelvic area causing a lot of pain.

I had administered an injection of morphine and was sitting at her bedside holding her hand.

"Margaret, as you look back on your life, what stands out the most for you?"

"Oh, I don't know," she said.

"Well, all these wonderful kids. Does that make your life

complete? Each one of them has turned out to be fine. Many of them making outstanding contributions in our society. Hasn't that knowledge given your life fulfillment?"

"Well, of course, I'm proud of each and every one of them, and I love being a mother, but my life is ending prematurely."

"How do you mean that?"

"I have a big regret."

"My goodness, Margaret. What could that be?"

"See," she eased herself over on her side and looked straight into my eyes, "I always wanted to be a nurse. I got married right after high school and started having babies, all these children, and now, here I am, dying, and I never got to be a nurse."

We both sat quietly.

I waited patiently for her next words.

"It isn't that my life is wasted. It's just that being a nurse was something I always wanted to do and now I'll never get to do it."

Then a light turned on in my head. "Wait a minute, Margaret! What does a mother do, anyway?"

"I don't know what you mean."

"Well, as a mother don't you wash and diaper and feed babies?"

"Yes, of course."

"And, as a mother, don't you put bactine and bandages on bruised elbows and knees?"

"Yes, sure."

"And, as a mother, don't you help kids with broken arms and bloody noses, and loose teeth, and . . ."

"And teach them nutrition and health," she chimed in.

"Right!" I exclaimed. "See those are many of the things nurses do. You just limited your practice to 105 Pine Street in Linglestown instead of a big hospital in Philadelphia."

"Right!" she beamed.

The morphine began to take hold. She lay back slowly on the pillows and closed her eyes, holding my hand tightly, gratefully. An easy smile came upon her face and she soon fell asleep.

She died that evening, surrounded by her husband and nineteen children praying, in unison, The Hail Mary.

The final story in this chapter, once again, serves as an example of second-guessing by a physician and how it affected a dying woman and the way she spent the last days of her life.

It was Christmas Eve day. I stood in the doorway of Miss Lane's room, watching her pack.

"I know who you are, Miss Ufema, I seen that show on the public television, but I don't need to talk with *you*. My doctor did surgery on me and he took out my whole pancreas and the tumor on top. Everything is going to be fine."

"I certainly hope so, Miss Lane."

At the desk, I saw her surgeon writing discharge orders. I shared with him the same words Miss Lane told me of what he supposedly told her.

"Sometimes patients hear only what they want to hear, so I simply am clarifying if you actually did tell her that you removed her pancreas." (I guess I'd been reading too many of my horse magazines instead of the JAMA, but I was positive about the human body not being able to maintain life without this vital organ.)

"That's right. That's what I told her."

"Well, it's a damn lie, isn't it?" I asked.

"Yes, but you don't want to ram it down her throat. She'll be back. I'll tell her then."

"I'm certainly not asking you to 'ram it down her throat' as you say, but to be gently honest with her about the seriousness of her illness."

"Yeh, well, she'll be back. I'll tell her then."

She did come back, but he didn't tell her. She was readmitted two months later, terminally ill. I had been sitting quietly by her side for over an hour. It was not necessary to study any laboratory results of her blood work to realize that death was imminent.

She withdrew her hand from mine and said, "You know, I had a really high temperature when I was home. Do you think that's why I'm so weak?"

"No, I don't, Helen."

She held my hand, closed her eyes, resting for a few moments before she asked again, "Do you think that really high fever is why I'm so weak now?"

"No, Helen, that isn't what I think."

I did not find it necessary to expound on what I did think. I sat quietly, waiting for her next words. "Why didn't he tell me?"

"Who tell you what, Helen?"

"The doctor. Why didn't my doctor just tell me I was going to die?"

"I don't know. Why do you think?"

"I don't know either, but I do know that if he would have told me, I'd have spent my last Christmas with my sister in Philadelphia." She went on to explain that she returned after surgery to her elderly parents' home. They too were ill and frail, barely able to open a can of soup, let alone care for their dying daughter. I also learned that there was no indoor plumbing in the house. (This explained in part why her condition was so advanced when she first visited a physician. Clay-colored stool is a definite symptom of trouble involving liver or pancreas. She never saw her stool due to using an outdoor latrine.)

"Helen, would you like me to call your parents to come here for one last visit?"

"Yes, please," she whispered.

I went out to the nurses' station and found her physician sitting at the desk writing belated admission orders. I asked to see Helen's chart for a moment to find the telephone number of her parents.

"Why do you want to call them?" he asked curtly.

"Because Helen wants them here."

He said nothing, rose, and walked away.

I dialed the number, but was rudely interrupted by the surgeon sticking his face directly in front of mine.

"I won't take responsibility if something happens to them."

Replacing the receiver, I asked him what he meant.

"Well, her folks are old, you know, and I don't know if they can handle this without something happening."

"I'm afraid I still don't understand what you're saying, Doctor."

"When you call and invite them to come here and witness these last hours — I mean I can't be responsible — *you'll* be responsible if one of those old people has a coronary or something!"

"That's pretty remote, wouldn't you say? Anyway, I'm willing to take that chance. They have the right to know their daughter is dying and asked for them. One last thought, Doctor, human beings are pretty tough critters. These elderly folks couldn't have lived this long without some trauma along the way and it looks to me like they've been coping quite adequately."

He turned and left, never visiting his patient.

I dialed the long-distance number again. After many rings, the phone was finally answered. A quavering voice said, "Hello?"

"Mrs. Lane, this is Harrisburg Hospital calling. Helen is still alive but she is very ill. She's been asking for you."

"Oh, dear." Then crying.

"Mrs. Lane, my name is Joy and I'm Helen's nurse. Would you like to come here for one, last visit?"

"Oh my goodness. Is she that bad?"

"Yes, Mrs. Lane, I'm sorry. Is there someone there who might drive you down?"

"Yes, my brother is here. He'll bring us." The conversation ended, and I was left with a dial tone.

Returning to Helen's room, I found her in semi-coma. I told her to hang on if she wanted, because her mother and father were on their way.

Helen spoke no final words. Her elderly parents got to her only minutes before she died.

She was pronounced dead by the surgical resident. Her own doctor never came near her.

Isn't it sad that he missed sharing a conversation that could have been beneficial, not only to his patient and her family, but also to himself?

Second-guessing, even in the name of protecting, is, in my opinion, condescending.

I recall a nursing instructor writing on the blackboard the word assume.

Marking a slash through the middle of the word she emphasized that "when we assume we only make an ass out of u and me."

MISSING PERSONS

THIS CHAPTER DISCUSSES A FEW PATIENTS WITH WHOM I HAD relationships of minimal breadth or depth. Regardless, they have every bit as much value as the other individuals I knew and loved. Like the others, in their own unique way, they too are teachers.

Mr. Brown was a patient with pancreatic carcinoma — notoriously painful and quick. I talked with him a bit. He was a little black gentleman who was not well educated. One afternoon he was discharged and didn't have a way home, so I took him to his house and got him squared away.

About one week later, he was re-admitted with intractable pain and constant vomiting. I was notified by Social Services that he was eligible for medical assistance. Carrying the necessary form with me, I entered his room to request his signature.

"Mr. Brown, this paper may be of importance to you. Why don't you look over it and if you want to receive medical assistance, just sign your name."

"I can't do that," he said quietly.

"You can't do what?" I asked.

"Neither of them things. I don't read so good and I can't sign. But I can make my mark."

"Fine, Mr. Brown, let me just sit down and go over this with you; then you can make your decision.

I began pointing out the main body of the paper when he said,

"So that's what my trouble is, huh, cancer? Right there, I can make out *that* word good enough, cancer."

"Didn't the doctor tell you before now?" I asked incredulously.

"No, they never told me nothing."

"Didn't you suspect something serious?"

"Yep, but I didn't let on."

"My goodness, why not?"

"Cause I didn't want to make my doctor feel bad." He lay back on his bed and shut his eyes.

"Would you like to share more of your feelings with me?" I asked hopefully.

"No, thanks anyway."

On Monday morning, I checked on him and learned that he signed himself out over the weekend. I stopped at his home, but no one answered the door.

Social Services was unable to locate him.

Joanne was one of those patients who shared easily. We talked openly for many hours about her feelings of being seriously ill.

"I want it to be over, but now that it's so close, I'm not sure. In fact, I'm afraid."

"How can I help?" I inquired.

"Oh, I know there's really nothing anyone can do."

"What is the worst thing about dying?"

She thought for a few moments before responding.

"Promise you won't laugh," she begged.

"I promise."

"Well, I guess most people would say the worst thing is leaving John and the kids. Maybe that's what I'm supposed to say."

"Joanne," I said, taking hold of her hand, "all you're supposed to say, if you want to share anything, is simply how you're feeling about dying."

"Okay, I guess I can trust you."

"You sure can," I assured her.

"The worst thing is this; you're looking at it."

I gazed around the living room, not sure at all what I was to see. "I'm afraid I don't understand," I confessed.

"Well, it's all this," she said with a weak sweep of her emaciated hand. "I finally got my favorite furniture and matching drapes and all, and now I've got to leave."

I didn't laugh, but I did smile.

So did Joanne.

She knew it was safe for her to share her personal loss without me superimposing my values upon her.

I always enjoyed Mr. Ackerman. In broken English, he would tell me stories about being a young boy when Nicholas was still Tsar of Russia. The first time we met was during rounds with the oncologists. They both were kind doctors, who allowed me to accompany them as they visited their many cancer patients.

On this particular day, we entered Mr. Ackerman's room to find him surrounded by medical personnel who were attempting to hold him down and insert an intravenous needle. He was screaming and shouting in Russian.

I moved to his bed in an attempt to disband the entourage and, hopefully, allow him the time and space to settle down and relax. As I placed my hand gently on his left arm I saw a tattoo of numbers. He was the right age, and a Russian Jew. Could it be possible that he had been detained in a concentration camp? If so, what horrible memories was he carrying with him to this particular hospital?

After a long half hour, he shared with me the origin of his tattoo. My deduction was accurate. He continued speaking and finally his behavior was explained.

Prior to this present admission, an alert was sent to all hospital staff that Heparin was extremely scarce — in fact, at a premium. The drug was to be used only on individuals who had developed blood clots and need anticoagulation.

Instead of inserting the usual tiny needle in the back of patient's hands, physicians were instructed to order the larger, more uncomfortable intravenous needles that did not require Heparin to prevent them from clogging.

Mr. Ackerman relaxed and became his usual trusting self after his oncologist assured him that his was a special situation, and for sure, he could have the little needle once again.

The remainder of his stay should have been uneventful. We were chatting leisurely one afternoon when he said, "My wife very, very sick."

"I didn't know you have a wife, Mr. Ackerman. She has never visited you here in the hospital."

"No, we are divorced. It was very bad time."

"Is Mrs. Ackerman at home?"

"No, here. Upstairs, here."

I called admissions office to learn her room number, then went to the tenth floor to visit. Her daughter was seated beside the bed, reading a newspaper. Mrs. Ackerman seemed comatose, and as I moved closer to examine her, I saw the tattoo on her left arm.

"Are you Sam's daughter?"

"Yes," she said curtly.

"And this is your mother?"

"Of course."

"How long has she been so sick?"

"About a month. Say, who are you, anyway?"

"I'm Joy Ufema, and I work exclusively with patients who are terminally ill."

"Is that how you know my father?"

"Yes."

"And did he tell you that we don't want to have anything to do with him?"

"No, he didn't."

"There are some very bad times that my mother needs to put behind her."

"She looks seriously ill. Is it possible to bury the hatchet?"

"I don't know what you mean."

"I can't begin to understand what you're going through and I don't need to know what transpired in the past, but perhaps you can allow some repair work to take place."

"How would you suggest I go about that?" She asked.

"You might start by allowing your father to share these final hours of your mother's life."

"You mean actually have him here in this room?"

"That's right. How would you feel about that?"

"I don't think I want him here."

I glanced at Mrs. Ackerman and realized that she could die at any moment. I felt her husband deserved the right to choose what he wanted to do. I excused myself and ran over to C-building.

Sam was sitting on his bed, reading a copy of *Soviet Life* that I brought him. "Sam, I need to talk with you."

"Da."

"Sam, Ruth is dying."

"Right dis minute?"

"Yes, do you want to be with her?"

"Da! Da! Hurry!"

He ran out of the room without putting on his slippers. Standing in front of the elevator, he shifted from one foot to the other. "Where is my Ruth? What Room?"

"She's on the tenth floor. I'll take you there."

As we entered the room, his daughter jumped up and said, "No, you can't come in here!"

"Why don't you go downstairs for a cup of coffee and leave him alone with her?" She allowed me to lead her past him, but looked back at him with a disgusted stare. Sam went over and sat down on Ruth's bed and wept. I closed the door.

He refused to leave when his daughter returned, so they kept watch together. Ruth died two hours later.

Being Jewish, they scheduled burial for the following day. I got Sam all shaved and dressed.

We sat in the lobby waiting for his daughter to take him to the funeral. She came through the door and handed him a necktie.

"This is for you to rend, Papa. You know, tear up, rip it, to show your grief."

"I know, already. Do you think I would forget about rending?"

She didn't respond but slipped her arm through his as they left the hospital.

I never saw him again.

I hope he and his daughter chose to forgive and forget the past and concentrate on repair.

Perhaps Ruth's death won't have been in vain.

11 *ANDY*

NDY WAS FOUR WHEN HE WAS DIAGNOSED WITH LEUKEMIA. I didn't really get close to him for a while. I'd just stop in and read a little bit. He'd had some cerebral hemorrhages, so he was blind in both eyes for a time. This was a great disadvantage, as I couldn't get him to draw pictures about his illness for me. Also, I think, it takes a while to develop a relationship with a child. With kids, we tend to take over as a surrogate mother — especially with dying children. What's important is for us to sustain the parents. He didn't want Joy, he wanted his mother. His mother was exhausted and going through a lot of stress. The best thing that I can do for Andy is to take his mother to the snack shop for a coke and let her cry.

I started seeing him a little bit more frequently. I stopped one morning about 6:30. It was winter and still dark when I got off the elevator and could hear crying in the pediatrics department. So I walked up to where they keep the sickest kids in the rooms off the glass cubicles of the nurses' station. Andy is crying and crying. I said, "What's the scene here?" "Well, he's been bawling all night, Joy." I said, "Well, why don't you hold him?" "You don't have to be here all night, Ufema, because if we go in and hold him, every time he bawls, he'll want you to go in and hold him, and then he'll start in bawling some more."

I said, "Yes, sometimes when I bawl I want to be held, too."

"Well, besides we have a lot of other sick kids here."

I said, "Yes, I can see you're out holding them."

I went in to him. Even though he was four and potty trained, he'd wet his pajamas because he'd regressed a lot. This little boy was very sick and he knew it. Now he's blind, he's crying, and he wants his mommy. And nobody's there. And even though he is blind, he knows it is night. This is really scary.

I said, "Andy, it's Joy."

"I want my mommy."

"I know you do, Andy, but you're stuck with me a little bit. How would you feel about me giving you a bath and getting your pajamas changed, and I have new pajamas here, and you could either put on the ones with the baseball players or with the cowboys."

That's giving a four year old a choice, some control over his environment. It's as much out of control as it can be. He said, "Okay."

So I bathed him and he chose the pajamas with the baseball players. I held him on my lap as we sat in the rocking chair.

Frequently I ask patients of all ages to draw pictures of themselves. I recall another child of five with leukemia.

"David, would you please draw me a picture of what you were like last year?"

And he drew a large head with eyes and a nose and big, smiling mouth. Then he took the black crayon and drew lots of hair.

"Thank you David. Next, could you please draw me a picture of what you're like *this* year?"

And he drew a head, much smaller than the first with eyes and a nose and an upside down smile, a frown, and no black hair because chemotherpy and radiation had caused it to fall out.

"Thank you, David. Last, could you please draw me a picture of what you'll be like next year?"

And he drew an empty bed.

I'm sure he meant he'd be dead. If he meant he would be well and not needing a sick bed I think he would have drawn himself playing and having black hair again.

Because Andy couldn't see well enough to draw, I needed to use other methods to help him express his feelings.

I said, "You know you have a stuffed bear here and little stuffed horse and they are your friends. The bear is very, very sick and the horse wants to know why the bear isn't sleeping at night.

He said, "I think I know."

I said, "Why, honey?"

"I think he's afraid."

I said, "Yes," What is your favorite animal?"

He said, "I like little cats."

I replied, "It's fantastic, because I have two little cats at my house right now and they want to come in and visit you and this bear, but you would have to sleep pretty good tonight, so that you'd be strong enough for the visit tomorrow. Do you think you could do that?"

"Yes."

Breakfast came, and then Mom and things got a little better for the day.

I thought maybe I'd better talk to the pediatric supervisor about these cats. Maybe I'd ask the pediatrician. Now wait a second here, what is the worst thing that could happen? The cat is going to bring in a disease and kill this lad? I don't think so. And besides it's between Andy and the cats. The cats agreed, so the next morning I came waltzing in carrying these two kittens in a towel.

I got by the nurses' station and the head nurse said, "Miss Ufema, there's a gray tail sticking out there!" Well, I threw the kittens in his crib and took my shoes off and crawled in with him. The nurses came back, and they were really neat. The cat ran up and down that little guy's tummy and finally settled down on the pillow and napped and purred. Andy is blind, but he could hear the therapy of a purring cat.

Leukemia has remissions and relapses. He would get better. And he'd been pretty good for a year.

One day, I was on my way down a corridor to go to lunch and I ran into an orderly with him in a little wheelchair, going to EEG. He was having seizures and cerebral involvement was suspected. Being blind, it took him a minute to recognize me by my voice. And my impulsiveness and my love for him made me go right up to him and uncover him from his blankets and grab him. Then I could see his face and I was just horrified at his condition. Total loss of hair, round face from the therapy, big spleen from it too, just sallow and no muscle tone. I turned my head; I was so upset. I told him I'd see him after his EEG and stay with him until he went to sleep.

Across the street from the hospital is the Susquehanna River, so I'd just plunk him in a wheelchair and take him the hell outside. He'd be in the hospital for 38 days in a row. He'd throw stones in the water. It was just wonderful. It would be hot out and I'd think this kid can't take it, I can't take it. But he would—he was just a gutsy little guy.

One particular afternoon we were traveling down the sidewalks of Harrisburg. We made a side trip to the courthouse where a large fountain sprayed water into a reflecting pool.

I'm sure it was all terribly illegal but nevertheless we took our shoes and slippers off, rolled out pantlegs up, and had a delightful time splashing and wading in this magnificent bubbling fountain. Of course, Andy had to be extra careful because he had an intravenous tubing in his left hand but what the heck, he had a few giggles in an otherwise painful and frightening day. It was during our return to the pediatric department that he said to me,

"Joy, do I have diabetes?"

"No, Andy, you don't."

"Well, do people who have diabetes, do they die?"

"Sometimes."

"Joy, do I have Leukemia?"

"Yes, buddy, you do."

"Do people who have Leukemia die?"

"Sometimes, darlin'."

"Am I going to die?"

"Maybe, Andy. We're having trouble getting your blood ok this time."

"If I'm going to die I want to go home." He stared down at his white hands.

"Okay, Andy. That's what we'll do.

I shared this conversation with his mother, Nancy.

"'Have I lost my remission?' And I said yes. Then he said,

'What are they gonna do now; are they going to give me more drugs?' And I said, No, Andy. There are no more drugs. He was real quiet for a minute, Joy, and then he said, 'Then I want to go home.'"

"That's exactly what we'll do, Nancy, and you've got yourself a live-in nurse if you want."

"Oh, Joy, I couldn'd do this without your help."

"Sure you could. I'm just being selfish because I love him."

During the next week or so he was doing fairly well.

My telephone rang and it was Andy calling.

"My mother told me you got a horse." he said, reprimanding me for not telling him immediately.

"That's right," I chuckled.

"Well, I think I ought to come over there and ride him."

"I think so, too, Andy. When?"

"Tomorrow." He knew.

The big Oldsmobile pulled in next to the barn. Nancy had to hold the heavy door open for him. A pair of too large, too new cowboy boots emerged. Inside them stood Andy, weak and pale but grinning.

I swung that little boy up in the saddle and he held on with what small amount of strength remained. Because, *we do what we need to do!* The more we walked around the pasture the more Andy drooped but he finished the ride.

In December my phone ran again. It was Nancy. Andy was hospitalized and bleeding badly. She wanted him home. Would I help?

I immediately left the supper table and drove to the hospital.

After numerous phone calls to contact the pediatrician he finally arrived.

Andy was conscious.

The doctor went over to him and said,

"Andy, do you know what's going on here?"

No answer.

"Andy," the doctor repeated.

"What?"

"Do you know what's going on here?"

A pause.

"Yes," he said, weakly.

"Well, Joy, said you want to go home. Is that right or do you want to stay here in the hospital?"

"I want to go home."

"Well, there's going to be a lot of bleeding, do you think your mother can handle that?"

I said, "Get out. Just write the prescriptions for pain medicine and get out!"

He got to the door, turned and said,

"Someone's going to have to be called to pronounce him dead."

"Don't worry, Doctor, we won't bother you." I hissed.

This pediatrician was a brilliant oncologist. He had juggled chemotherapy for Andy so well that he kept him alive for three years, but I think he lost the whole ball game during those few minutes at the bedside.

His only sin was he loved the boy! So I might have asked him,

"Doctor, what's the worst thing that could happen?"

He might have replied, "I'm hurting so much over losing him, I might start to cry in front of him."

"Right! That's all right. At least Andy knows you love him!"

But the Doctor couldn't, or wouldn't, simply be real. Both he and Andy lost.

The ambulance driver entered Andy's hospital room. He had on white cover-alls with a black and red hunting jacket. A big bear of man with a full, black beard.

With huge, but gentle hands he picked the little boy into his arms so that none of Andy's fragile bones hurt. And this big bear of a guy carried the dying child out into the winter night all bundled up in a blue, wool blanket, and laid him down on the bed in the ambulance.

"Joy," Andy said, "Would you ride in here with me, please?"

"Of course, but, you know your mom is used to driving that big, automatic Oldsmobile. I'll prop you up so maybe you can keep watch over her in *my* truck."

We both giggled a bit as we watched the bobbing headlights of my truck as Nancy, struggling with the clutch, hopped along the highway.

Although it was dark and Andy had never completely recovered his sight he used sixth sense to call my attention to landmarks in Perry County. This would be his last ride and he bravely shared favorite places with me that he could never again enjoy.

After forth-five minutes we arrived home, in New Bloomfield.

The black-bearded ambulance driver picked up the exhausted body and carried him to his bedroom, with the racecar wallpaper. His little dog jumped on the bed and remained until the next morning when Andy awoke in pain.

During Saturday he had a few visitors, one piece of jelly bread, and three intravenous administrations of Demerol to ease the pain. I hurt for him, that he had to suffer, just to die.

About two a.m. Nancy could hardly stay awake.

"Go to bed," I told her. "I'll call you if he worsens. It's safe for you to sleep. No one could give him better care than what he'll receive from me."

Reluctantly she laid down and in moments fell asleep.

Andy seemed to be resting comfortably. I was reading.

"Are there ponies where I'm going?" he quietly questioned.

"There are magnificent ponies where you're going." I replied.

"Will I be able to hang-glide?"

"Oh, yes, all over the place." He fell asleep.

About four o'clock I heard Andy's father leave the master bedroom.

"How's he doing?" he asked groggily.

"He's quiet, Paul. I don't think he's having any pain."

Nancy was awakened by the conversation.

"What time is it?" she asked.

"It's about four. Do you want some coffee?" Paul answered.

"Yea, I'll fix us some. Joy, why don't you sleep awhile?"

"All right. Call me in a few hours."

By 6:30 Andy was much worse and by 10 a.m. he was moments from death.

We were gathered around his bed, witness to his courage, weeping.

Nancy said to her son, "Andy, I'm holding your left hand and Jesus is holding your right hand so that at no point before you cross over will you be without somebody holding your hand."

And then he died.

There was no big episode of bleeding or panic. I won't say the whole thing was a good experience because of the tragic loss, but I've seen hundreds of people die and he was the champion.

The people who loved him loved him enough to make some semblance of worth out of his living and dying. None of us could halt his death but we chose to have the event happen as painlessly and with as much dignity as possible.

The same physician who delivered him into this world pronounced him dead.

KING OF THE GYPSIES

DURING MY LUNCH HOUR I RAN DOWNTOWN TO BUY SOME beads for a little girl with leukemia. She was ten years old and had been in the hospital for six weeks. I had visited with her during many difficult hours, and we had developed a trusting relationship. She even allowed cameras to film her during a documentary on my work for WTOP from Washington.

Still very ill, she had at least rallied enough to sit up, eat ice cream, and exert a desire to string a bead necklace. Her request smacked of urgency. I ate a sandwich while browsing through Fitch's Indian Trading Post. My selection of beads must be perfect. Smugly, I resolved to wear her necklace always, in honor of her soldiering in the battle of cancer.

Leaving the store I saw and heard a commotion on the steps of the capitol building. Through the crowd, I saw the body of a man, slumped on the sidewalk. Darting between cars I ran across the street.

"What happened?" I shouted.

Seeing my white uniform, a middle-aged woman pushed me through the throng. A lady who appeared to be the gentleman's wife was sobbing and grasping him by the shirt. He was unconscious.

"Roscoe, Roscoe, get up!" she wailed.

I felt his neck, searching for a carotid pulse. None. I put my cheek to his mouth. No exchange of air.

Quickly measuring four inches from his sternum to the middle of his chest, I hit him over his heart with a strong fist.

Pointing to a white-haired, distinguished man in a topcoat, I commanded ... "Sir, call an ambulance, quick."

Moving to the patient's blue face, I opened his mouth to remove any foreign particles before initiating mouth-to-mouth resuscitation. On a few occasions I have removed dentures, particals, and even vomitus, but on this January day, crouched on the cold steps of Harrisburg's capital building, I beheld something so astounding that it paralyzed me for valuable seconds. In his left incisor was a diamond and in his right incisor was a ruby.

I was jolted back to reality by a woman announcing to me that she was a nurse.

"Get started breathing for him and I'll do cardiac massage."

"Huh? Oh, yeah."

We worked for about fifteen minutes. Placing my fingers under his chin, I felt a pulse.

"We've got him!" I said then, "Where the hell is that ambulance?"

"It's coming up State Street now," someone called.

As the paramedics loaded him in the ambulance, the patient's wife pulled on my arm and whispered hoarsely, "Praise God you were here! You've saved my Roscoe, the King of the Gypsies!" With that proclamation she climbed in the back of the ambulance and sped off to the emergency room.

Startled a bit, I walked back to the hospital to deliver the beads to Tracy.

"Thank you, Miss Ufema," she said through bleeding gums. "I'm gonna make this necklace for someone I love."

Her mother winked at me as I left the child's room, smiling inside and out.

Piercing my state of contentment, the voice over the public address system blasted forth the edict, "CASE ONE IN EMERGENCY ROOM! CASE ONE, CASE ONE—EMERGENCY ROOM."

I walked quickly to the stairway then ran down the steps two at a time. Above and below I heard other medical team members racing to the ER.

Most of us arrived simultaneously. While nurse anesthetists and second-year residents worked on the recumbent patient, I went to the waiting room to search for family.

"Oh dear God, Nursie, it's you again. Help my Roscoe!"

Jumping from her chair was the woman from the capitol steps. The lady who said her husband was King of the Gypsies.

"My name is Joy. What is yours please?"

"Tallis, that is my husband Roscoe. He was okay in the ambulance. Then we got here and they told me to wait here. Now he went bad again. Oh Nursie, please do again for him what you did before."

Mrs. Tallis, the doctors and nurses are with him now. Sit down, if you can, and I'll go see what has happened."

"Oh, dear God, thank you, thank you."

I left her sitting on the couch, wrapping a white lace handkerchief around her fingers.

Entering the main arena of the emergency room, I walked past a burly young redhead who appeared to have severed his hand in a bad accident.

On a litter lay a little gray-haired lady covered with a blanket stamped River Rescue Ambulance.

In the corner cubicle sat a young mother holding her toddler tightly while a physician examined the little boy's leg.

I walked over to the bed surrounded by medical and nursing personnel. The monitor on the wall revealed the patient to be experiencing ventricular fibrillation. At least he had a heart beat, even though it was erratic and too rapid.

"Gimme another amp of bicarb," barked the senior resident.

Each team member followed orders quickly and quietly. In a miraculous few moments the patient stabilized.

"Okay," said the resident, "let's get this guy up to intensive care, and quick!"

"Dr. Hooper," I interrupted, "how's Mr. Tallis doing?"

"He's holding his own for now, but I can't predict what might happen in the near future."

"Okay, I've got his wife outside. I'll take her over to Admitting so we can get some information."

"Great, Joy, thanks."

After turning Mrs. Tallis over to the kind girls in the admission office, I asked if she would like me to call any family members.

"I already called by two daughters, Nursie. They'll be here soon."

"All right then, I'll see you a little later in the waiting room at the Intensive Care Unit."

I walked the two flights up to Pediatrics to check on Tracy's progress with my bead necklace.

She lay on her right side, facing the door, and appeared to be sleeping. Her mother, in stocking feet, was curled up in the lazy-boy recliner. I tiptoed into the room and gently covered them both with light blankets. As I turned to go, I noticed the primitive necklace of red, white, yellow, and blue beads on the overbed table. Beside it, on a piece of lined notebook paper, was the message in crayon. To Dr. Garcia, with love — Tracy.

So, it was not to be mine. She loved her doctor.

Momentarily disappointed, I sighed and then left the room. Then it occurred to me how grateful he would be. Guilty and saddened over not being able to save her, he would at least be sure that she understood and forgave him.

I walked up the back steps to the waiting room to investigate the status of Mr. Tallis. Lining the corridor were gypsies. Sitting all over the stairs were gypsies. There were gypsies in the waiting room, gypsies in the linen room, and gypsies in the nurses' lounge. I side-stepped my way through the group till I found Mrs. Tallis.

She introduced me to a tall, dark, handsome young man wearing a black, cashmere overcoat.

"How do you do?" he said, with an unfamiliar accent. "My name is David. I am next in line to be King. These are my people. We are all Rumanians."

I stammered a bit, then finally succeeded in asking my question. "Why are there so many folks here?"

"Because Roscoe is our King. We must all stay with him now. And when he dies I must be with him and light a candle so his spirit can rise to Heaven."

"I see. Ah, David," I was speaking slowly, not sure what to say next. "As you are well aware, because of the oxygen tubes in most of these patients, we could never allow an open flame to be present in the ICU."

Removing his coat to reveal an exquisite silk suit, he looked at me intently.

"Joy, we do not want our King to die; we do not want any trouble, but we must maintain the tradition that has been carried out for centuries by our people. I must be present at the time of death. A candle must be lit. That is all. Excuse me."

With a European flair, he placed his coat, like a cape, over his shoulder, and turned, and strutted from the room.

Mrs. Tallis was crying. Two heavy-set women in high, black boots and flowered skirts sat on either side of her, cooing, comforting in a language I had never heard.

Stepping over and around gypsies of all sizes, shapes, and ages, I made my way to the double doors of the Intensive Care Unit.

I walked over to bed seven and looked at this King of the Rumanian gypsies. He was asleep. A small, green hose offered oxygen to him through his nose. His left hand was taped to secure an intravenous line through which glucose water and drugs dripped. His color was poor, his breathing shallow. Glancing up at the monitor, I saw a jagged line on the screen revealing his too-slow, irregular pulse. Neither the ruby nor the diamond could buy him a healthy heart. What really was of value, now, was his quality of life and his dignity in death.

I needed no crystal ball to predict his future. He simply could not go on living in this deteriorated condition. What would help him and his family most? Maintaining tradition at death as they did during life. Suddenly it came to me.

I dashed to the phone and paged Dr. Williams. After explaining the wishes of his patient's family regarding a lighted candle, I then shared with him my idea. He agreed and dictated a verbal order. I took the chart to the Head Nurse who co-signed it, smiling.

Greatly relieved, I went in search of David in the hospital cafeteria. I found him sitting at a large table surrounded by ten or twelve men. As I approached, he rose.

"Is Roscoe all right?" he asked, urgently.

"Yes, David, for the moment. I think I've come up with a solution to our problem."

"Please, sit down. Would you like anything to eat or drink?"

"No, thank you, I'm on my way home. What I want you to know is that if Roscoe begins to have another cardiac arrest, the nurses have orders to wheel his bed away from the oxygen and pull him out in the hall where it's safe to light the candle. How would that be?"

He spoke slowly. I was wishing for more praise and enthusiasm over my brilliant idea.

"Roscoe has not regained consciousness?"

"No," I said quietly.

"Is there a chance he will?"

"I don't know. We certainly could ask his doctor."

"Well, until he does wake up and can talk, we want *everything* done that can be done. If he has another one of those arrests we don't want you to just disconnect him and wheel him out in the hall. We want the doctors to keep him alive until he regains consciousness. Got it?"

My memory recalled too many patients in similar circumstances. Due to the reluctance on the part of families or physicians to accept death, orders are given to resuscitate the patient each and every time he went into cardiac arrest. I remembered a particulary favorite gentleman who had been one of my first patients on the urology floor. Years later, he lay in the Intensive Care Unit, unable to speak for himself. After twelve resuscitative experiences, he was finally dying. His sternum and several ribs were broken as the result of an aggressive resident who thought himself an expert at external cardiac massage. The patient's heart muscle had turned mushy from too many attacks, and he arrested three and four times daily. Still no order from his physician to cease resuscitation. His wife wanted it stopped. The physician said, "No, I won't play God," yet, he was playing God! With great courage, one of the nurses on night duty did not call case one. She simply pulled the curtain around his bed and held his hand for the few moments it took for him to die.

As the scene played over in my mind, I finally responded.

"Why is this so important? I'm certainly not advocating active euthanasia, but Roscoe is terminally ill. Why is it necessary to put him through all this?"

"The reason is not your business," David began. "Your business is to follow the orders of the doctor, and his business is to follow the orders of this family."

"I see," I said, coolly. "Very well, I'll get the order rescinded."

"You do that, thank you."

After notifying the supervisor of the change and receiving her promise to take care of everything, I drove home.

Sometime around 2 a.m. I was awakened by a ringing telephone. It was the ICU secretary telling me there were now 73 gypsies in the hall and waiting room and where were they going to put them? There had been a bit of a ruckus over too many gypsies at the patient's bedside, so David asked her to call me. In the interim, Mr. Tallis had cased twice and had been resuscitated. He had suffered severely and was attached to a ventilator. Obviously, his medulla, the center in his brain that regulates breathing, had been damaged. Things didn't look good.

"Look, Evelyn, send some of the folks downstairs to the Social Service family room and see if Joan can get some cots from the Blood Bank. I'll be in around seven."

As I approached the ICU waiting room I heard muffled cries. Thinking Roscoe must have died, I followed the sound. It was coming from the women's lavatory. Opening the door, I bumped into several gypsies. Sitting in a chair in the middle of the bathroom was a very pregnant woman rocking in pain.

"Her water! She broke!" screamed one of the ladies.

I dashed down the hall into the operating room lounge and grabbed an orderly and litter.

"Gimme a hand, quick!"

"Hey, wait a second, I ain't done readin' about Stevie Wonder!"

"Forget Stevie Wonder and help me get this lady on the litter!"

"Oh, hell!" he said, "She's not goin' to have a baby right here 'n now, is she?"

His eyes were large and he was thrusting his hands in and out of his pockets.

"She is if you don't get moving! Help me lift her up!"

We succeeded in stabilizing the young woman on the litter.

"Take her down to the emergency room, fast. You, ladies, please go along."

"Yes, yes," they replied in unison. I sighed with relief as they disappeared into the elevator.

"That's all we need around here," I mumbled, "one more gypsy."

For the next several days things were uneventful. That is if having 104 gypsies from ten different countries can be termed uneventful.

There were several minor incidents. Like the children removing all the ice cream and popsicles from the freezer in the cafeteria, or that small fire in the Social Service family room, or the knowledge gleaned by the admission office that the social security number given for Roscoe Tallis was fictitious. All of these seemed to pale in relation to the finale unfolding before us.

While lecturing to the X-ray therapy class, I was interrupted by the Assistant Director of Nurses. It seems everything was coming to a head and David demanded to speak only with me.

As we walked beside the frozen Susquehanna River, he clarified his earlier behavior.

"You see, Joy, Roscoe actually is King of the Rumanian gypsies. That means he, and he alone, holds the finances of our people. None of us know the exact worth, but we're sure it is five, maybe six figures. For obvious reasons, we do not believe in banks, so only Roscoe knows where the money is. He's forbidden to even tell his wife."

"So, that's why you wanted all attempts to keep him alive, so he could tell you where the money is?"

"Precisely. Unfortunately, his doctor tells me he is never going to be conscious again."

"I'm truly sorry, David. How can I help?"

He kicked ice from his Gucci loafers. Then stood quietly, looking up the river.

"We've all agreed to pull the plug and relieve the hospital of any responsibility."

"That must have been a terrible, difficult decision for you. I guess, as the new King, you're getting a Baptism by fire, so to speak."

He smiled, but didn't laugh.

"Yes, I guess you might say that. Anyway, you've been so kind, could you please take care of the final details and let me know when everything is ready?"

"Of course, I'll get started immediately."

We transferred Roscoe to a medical floor, received the results of his third, flat, EEG, then instructed anyone who wished, to visit him and say goodbye. It took two and one-half hours. Suddenly, a scream from his daughter. We rushed into the room and found Roscoe experiencing another cardiac arrest. I looked at David who shouted, "The candle! Light the candle!"

"Not in here," I said, "quick, help me pull the bed out in the hall."

Several nurses and a respiratory specialist unplugged the respirator and pushed the bulky bed out of the room. He was instantly surrounded by gypsies. I couldn't see what was happening, but I heard the striking of a match.

A few weeks later, as I leaned against the wall reading a thank-you note from David, Dr. Garcia walked by wearing a beaded necklace and a big grin. I smiled too, for as bad as it all seemed some days, deep in my heart, I knew it was all worth the many pains.

WE DIE THE WAY WE LIVE

MRS. MCCASKEY WAS ONE OF MY FIRST PATIENTS. SHE WAS 45 years old and had cancer of the tongue and pharynx. Her physician strongly suspected the disease was caused by her smoking four packs of cigarettes a day since she was the age of ten. In spite of a quiet sadness about her, she as a tough little broad. She had grown up in a rough city and had developed a hard shell.

She had one son who would visit regularly. He didn't seem able to be emotionally supportive but at least he would sit by her bed for several hours twice a day.

Due to the location and extensive involvement of the malignancy, Mrs. McCaskey couldn't speak. She communicated by scribbling notes.

One afternoon I was visiting with her, mesmerized as she held a Lucky Strike cigarette up to her throat where a tracheotomy had been performed.

Smoke would be drawn in through the little silver tube in her throat, and she would occasionally look at me and smile.

I refrained from passing judgment. Tobacco was her only pleasure, now, as it had been throughout her life. If she quite smoking that very day her dying would not be halted.

She took up her little green spiral notebook and a stubby yellow pencil and wrote: "Tell me the truth. Am I dying?"

I touched her hand, looked into her cold, brown eyes and said, "Yes."

She wrote: "How soon?"

I said, "I don't konw."

"Can you help me do it sooner than you think it might be?" she scribbled.

"No, Edna, I'm not comfortable doing that."

She stubbed out the Lucky Strike, then leaned back on her pillows.

"Would you like to share with me how you're feeling about dying?" I asked.

She kept her eyes closed and shook her head "no."

"Would you like me to stay with you a little longer?"

Eyes shut, she shook her head "no."

I left quietly.

A week later I rode beside her in the ambulance to Philadelphia where she was transferred to the Sacred Heart Home for the Incurable Cancer Patient.

She died within a month, among strangers. She never wrote another note during the remainder of her life. She shut all of us out of her heart. Later, her son told me how she had always been an abrasive "wise-guy." Even when a friend would take a chance on getting close to her she would become cynical and respond to a warm gesture with sarcasm.

She made no investments in life for death. Of course, to do that, she would have had to acknowledge that she was going to die, sometime, and to develop a few relationships that would be supportive and offer comfort.

Building this kind of quality friendship, however, requires commitment. It means becoming involved, reciprocating, sharing good and bad times, and being dependable. I look at it as bread upon the water.

The following anecdote reflects a similar personality. A story, rather sad, of another woman struggling with the day-to-day effort of living with cancer.

I had been working as a thanatologist nurse for about six months when I was requested to see Bev. She was under the services of our Intern-Resident program due to her poor socio-economic status. Perusing her chart I learned that she was 32 years old, had both breasts removed within the past 36 months and was currently admitted to the hospital because of uncontrollable bone pain from the spread of her disease.

Entering the four-bed room I found her sitting up in bed, wearing a hospital gown, hair in braids decorated with bows made from surgical gauze and reading a movie magazine.

"Hi, Bev. My name's Joy. Do you feel like talking?"

"What about?"

"Your feelings about having cancer."

"There ain't much to tell," she said. "I got it and it's gonna kill me."

Taken by surprise at her bluntness, I stammered, then asked how she felt about having to die at such a young age.

"It ain't all that bad," she said, then returned to flipping pages in the magazine.

"Hey, what time is it, anyway?" she asked.

"It's ten minutes of two, why?

"My story that I like is on at two. I don't have no money to pay to have this here TV, but one of them social workers paid for it. People sure are nice, aren't they?"

"Yes, they sure are."

A funny feeling had crept inside me. A new feeling, considering the circumstances. I was jealous that someone else was meeting one of her needs. I was quickly getting caught up in feeling sorry for her and experiencing some vague sense of guilt for not having cancer, or at least for being healthy!

Over the next few days these emotions began manifesting themselves in behavior. I reminded Bev that she was to page *me* if she needed anything. I found myself running to the snack or gift shops to purchase any little whim she might mention "just in passing."

Her birthday was on a Friday; how convenient, it was also payday. I talked the nurses into pitching in for a cake, more magazines, cards, and another week of paid television. The whole thing seemed quite harmless. Bev seemed to be enjoying the attention, and I was feeling mysteriously less guilty about being 32 years old with a happy life ahead.

I proudly placed my two gifts on her bed. She opened the smaller one first.

"Oh, a watch; it's real pretty."

"Well, I thought you might need one so you can know when it's two o'clock."

"Huh?"

"You know, two o'clock .... for your story," I explained, pointing to the television.

"Oh, yea."

"Gee, I hope you like this other little present."

Silently she opened the wrapped music box.

"It plays Eidleweiss, you know, from the Sound of Music."

"Yeah, Joy, it's real nice."

"Look, would you like me to help put your watch on for you?"

"Sure," she said, smiling.

The next morning the phone was ringing in my office as I was removing my coat.

"This is Joy Ufema," I answered.

"Yeah, it better be Joy Ufema, this is Betty Reed down on 4."

"Oh, hi, Betty. What's up? Is Bev all right?"

"She's more than all right. You were so nice to get her that watch that now she's timing exactly, to the minute, when her next pain injection is due, and if we're late with it, like last evening, she tells Dr. Kelly."

"I see," I said, scratching my head.

"So thanks so much for your generosity. Goodbye."

"Goodbye, Betty."

"Isn't that too bad," I thought. "Those darn nurses. They don't even feel sorry for Bev." I just couldn't understand it.

Later on that day I would begin to understand.

I was paged by the oncology resident who told me Bev was being discharged in the afternoon. After lunch I stopped by her room. She was packing.

"Hi. So you're splittin' the joint, huh?"

"Yeah, and I'm glad, too."

"Did you get your prescription for the Demerol tablets for pain?"

"Yeah. Hey Joy, could you go to the pharmacy downstairs and get this prescription filled for me?"

"Gee, I'm sorry, Bev. The hospital doesn't do that anymore."

"Well, I guess Dick will just have to stop on our way home, somewhere, but I ain't got no idea where." She looked at me with forlorn eyes. "You wouldn't know where, would ya, Joy? I'm on this public assistance, you know." (More puppy eyes).

"No, Bev, I don't know, but I'll call Social Service. They'll know."

Something just didn't feel right, but I couldn't put my finger on it.

Attempting to compensate for the prescription failure, I inquired, "So, is there anything I can do for you before you leave?"

"Yeah, there is one thing."

"Sure, Bev, what is it?"

"Well, I was wondering ..."

"Yes?"

"I was wondering if you could get me a swimming pool."

"A swimming pool?" I asked, incredulously.

"Not for me, for my kids. You know, one of them big plastic swimming pools for out in the yard."

"Bev, I can't do that. That's not what I'm for."

"Well what the hell good are ya then, anyway?" she shouted. "You asked me what I wanted and I told ya, but no, no, 'That ain't what you're for.' Well, you can just forget it lady!"

She grabbed the brown grocery bag that was serving as a suitcase. Walking up the hall she told one of the nurses' aides that she was ready to be taken downstairs.

I stood, shaking my head in disbelief. Then I noticed it on the bedside stand, beside the telephone. She had taken the plastic cup and water pitcher but had left the music box.

About a month later the social worker told me she had been admitted to a nursing home in York County. Her husband did not choose to raise the two youngest children. Bev had alienated herself from any family or friends who might be potential candidates as surrogate parents. Both the social worker and I visited her and worked together to get the children placed in a foster home.

She lived a long, miserable year. She carried the grudge about the swimming pool until her dying day.

As I look back on this experience, I realize how Bev's death was a continuum of her life. She had poorly developed coping mechanisms. Every time life presented her with stress, she would get sick or exhibit manipulative behavior. Sometimes it would work. For the most part it did not. My attempts to buy her off were very immature and obviously ineffective. For me, her dying was not without benefit. I learned to be more open and direct with patients and to deal more honestly with my feelings regarding *their* behavior.

I think you'll see how this change took place in the following case.

Unlike Mrs. McCaskey and Bev, Miss Carlson was financially quite well-to-do. She was a retired nurse who had worked for the state.

She had a private room in the hospital both because she was a private person and because she had a malignant tumor in her jaw that had eroded away half of her face.

Most of us were a bit intimidated by her, but I persisted. Mainly because she literally had no one.

She had a sign on her door that read No Visitors. I suppose it was to convince us that she had so many friends that she would need to restrict them from innundating her room. Perhaps, too, it served as a buffer to her that if she forbid friends from visiting, she could always delude herself that someone might have come. She just would never know for sure. It would have been too painful to have no sign and no visitors.

She was quite spunky, however, and insisted on dressing the wound herself. It was quite disfiguring and had an unpleasant odor. I suggested she soak the bandages in buttermilk before applying them. It helped.

I would always knock before entering and wait for her response.

"Who's there?"

"It's Joy, Miss Carlson."

"What do you want?"

"I wondered if you'd like some company."

A pause.

"Oh all right. Come in."

I'd give her a big grin and then pull a chair up to the side of her bed. She was never rude, just cautious.

"How is your pain today?"

"Much less, thanks." She was constantly dabbing at her chin with a handkerchief. Saliva oozed incessantly.

"So, what should we talk about?" I teased.

"You're the one who wanted to visit. I was perfectly content to just lie here."

What do you think about all day?" I asked.

"Oh, mostly about my work with the state," she replied.

"Tell me about it, if you feel like it."

"There's really not that much to tell."

"I'm genuinely interested, Miss Carlson."

"Well, I just worked for the State Board of Nurse Examiners. That's all."

"So *you're* the one responsible for me having diarrhea for three days last year!"

"I suppose." She smiled a painful, crooked smile.

"Did you like your work?"

"As much as anyone does, yes."

"Tell me about you," I tested.

"What?"

"Tell me about who you are."

"I'm nobody. I was born, I became a nurse, and now I'm going. What more is there? That's all."

"I mean tell me what makes you unique from every other human being in the world."

She wouldn't take the bait. Or couldn't. She didn't feel unique; therefore, she wasn't. I tried again. "What mark would you say you'll leave?"

"Mark? Just the mark on my tombstone, except there won't even be that. I want my body cremated.

"What about your ashes?" I asked, with some trepidation.

"Whatever. I think they dispose of them right at the place, the crematorium."

"Wouldn't you want them scattered someplace special or buried with a tombstone with your name?"

"No, nothing. Just disposed of. It's in my will."

The evening nurse came in the room to check Miss Carlson's vital signs. I excused myself and asked if I might return the next day.

She nodded yes.

Reading her chart, I noticed the next day was her birthday.

I made arrangements with the dietary department to send a cake along with her luncheon tray. Later that afternoon I returned to her room to say goodbye. Nurses, changing shifts, bustled up and down the hall.

After repeating the knocking ritual, I sat on the edge of her bed.

"So, Miss Carlson, tomorrow is your birthday."

"My last," she said, matter-of-factly.

"Perhaps," I acknowledged. "Therefore, what kind of gift would give you pleasure?"

"Nothing. I don't want a thing."

"Would it be disconcerting to you if I told you I'd really enjoy giving you a little something?"

"No, I just don't think it's necessary for you to go to that bother."

"But I want to. I genuinely like you and would like to brighten your birthday just a bit."

"Do whatever you'd like," she said, with a distorted grin.

Later that evening I stood in the middle of a very large shopping mall with no idea where to begin. As I browsed from one store to another, it became clear to me that I didn't know her well enough to make a purchase. She just hadn't shared openly or intimately about who she was as a person. I didn't know if she liked cats or cars, turtles or trees, the ocean or Agatha Christie. I spotted a medium-sized print in a chrome frame. It was a painting of a dense rain forest, dark green and black. Fog rose from the ground and shrouded the thick tree trunks. From out of the darkness and heavy dew, a sliver of light pierced the center of the picture. It seemed symbolic. After making my purchase, I hurried to a phone and called the hospital.

"Kim, this is Joy. Have you given Miss Carlson her sleeping pill?"

"No, not yet. Why?"

"Hold off for about fifteen minutes. I'm on my way with a birthday present."

It was rather difficult to wrap the gift while driving. For the first time in my life I found red stop lights beneficial. Due to the late hour I was able to park directly in front of the hospital. Riding to the eleventh floor, I felt better about this birthday gift than Bev's. I wasn't buying Miss Carlson off because I felt sorry for her and was guilty for being healthy. I felt a genuine sincerity in giving — no strings attached. I liked the print, I hoped she would, but it was okay if she didn't. That simple. The present was being given unconditionally.

In my excitement I failed to knock. Bursting through the door I saw her sitting crossed-legged, like a frail, mutated Buddah, on top of her pillow with her back leaning against the wall. She was dabbing at her chin with a kleenex trying to soak up the incessant drip of saliva. There was a definite twinkle in her eye.

"It's midnight," I said, "Happy Birthday, Miss Carlson."

"Thank you," she struggled, then reached for the gift I was offering.

With surprising strength she ripped open the ribbon and taped paper. With great excitement she tore away the covering to seek the prize. Then she seized the picture and held it out before her. Emaciated arms trembled at the demand to maintain position while her eyes scrutinized every detail of the painting. Breathless, I waited.

"It's perfect," she garbled.

"I'm glad you like it," I said.

"Please set it on the bureau so I can see it."

I complied.

As if suddenly thrust back to reality she grabbed up several tissues and began swabbing her chin. She kept up this work never taking her gaze from the painting.

"I need sleep now," she announced while skooting down in bed and under the covers.

"Would you like me to get you anything?"

"No."

"Then goodnight, Miss Carlson, and Happy Birthday."

"Goodnight, Miss Ufema. Thank you."

As I turned to leave I saw her dabbing a clean tissue to her eyes.

A few days later she was discharged. Home was an apartment complex with windows she never opened. Central heat or air conditioning kept her safe from the naturalness of life. Her balcony was unused. She never chose to sit outside during the evening hours; she kept the drapes drawn and doors locked. She missed the coo of the mourning doves, but she didn't, couldn't miss death. It came, the only friend she knew, in the hour before dawn. It's assistant was cancer, eroding into her carotid artery in her neck. She lay on her stomach, arms and legs flailing, swimming, as her life's blood spurted out onto sheets and pillows and speckled onto the picture of a dark green rain forest.

DON'T LET THE STARS GET IN YOUR EYES

"**O**KAY, THEN, WE'RE SET FOR WEDNESDAY MORNING. I'll bring my best photographer, he used to be with the White House."

I guess I wasn't too impressed, after all, the Harrisburg paper had done a write-up about my work. It was neat that the reporter had contacted me, and he was with the Washington Post, still and all, I wasn't too impressed.

His name was B.D. Colen, and he was a nice enough chap. The entire day was spent with him interviewing me about why I chose death and dying as a specialty, what intrinsic rewards I gleaned, and how many wars were fought with the antiquated system. He forced me to dig, to reach deep inside and scrutinize motives and values.

The photographer took hundreds of snapshots throughout the day. I was barely able to avoid his invading shutter even when nature called for me to empty my longago, too-full bladder.

Over all the day went well, and I enjoyed it. We all shook hands, smiled graciously and departed in different directions.

"I'll try to squeeze it in for either this Sunday's or next Sunday's edition. Thanks again, Joy."

I waved goodbye and went about locking my office door.

"Hmm," I mused, walking slowly down the steps. "It'll probably be lost in one of the segments headed 'Montage'. I'll probably be stuffed in between the marriage announcements and a short article on preparing crab legs."

Sunday morning I strolled rather casually outside the book

store, briefly running my finger over an edition of the *Washington Post*. I nonchalantly picked up the paper, placed sixty cents beside the cash register, and said to the clerk, "That's for the *Post*."

She nodded.

I walked out, holding the door for a lady behind me then walked to my parked truck. I could contain myself no longer. Jerking open the door, I jumped into the seat and began riffling through the paper. I threw the finance section aside, followed by classifieds, sports, and the Book Review. With frantic fervor I seized the Montage section and flipped the pages. Nothing. I might have missed it. I scrutinized a second time. No story, no picture. Perhaps it's in another section of the paper! Right! After fifteen minutes of careful looking, I acknowledged that it simply had not appeared this week. Anyway, what's there to get excited about?

A phone call from B.D. on Wednesday confirmed the date.

"Hi, Joy. Listen, it's all set for this Sunday's edition. Let's see, that would make it August 24, 1975. Your big debut! Hope you like it."

"I'm sure it's fine, B.D., thanks for calling."

Again the following Sunday, I arrived at the book store. I strolled, once more, over to the racks holding a dozen or so Sunday papers. I picked one up and began to make my purchase when I discovered it was *The Washington Star,* certainly a reputable newspaper, it just wasn't *my* paper. I returned it to the stand, spotted *The Washington Post* and picked up a copy.

Squatting on the floor of the store I laid the paper down. Folded in half I saw the face of the Greek dictator Papadopoulos. Instead of opening the paper up, I turned it completely over and began, from the back, slowly turning one page after another. No story, no picture. I was turning from page three to page two.

"Damn!" I thought, "He said it would be today."

And it was! I turned page two over and on the bottom of the front page, *under* Papadopoulos was a fantastic picture of me and the beginning of the article. I sat, staring at the page, grinning, and terribly impressed. I think the pleasure was not over publicity, rather over the pride that my work and philosophy as affirmed. Death and dying is such a nebulous field. It has no handbook of absolutes to follow. I was doing what I thought was right, but it was rewarding to see others concur.

I stood up, picked up three more copies of the paper, and took them to the register. Laying the thick newspapers on the counter, I made sure Papadopoulos was face down and my picture was facing front.

"Okay," she said, "four copies at sixty cents, that comes to $2.40. I handed her three dollars and pushed the papers closer to her. She counted out the change then looked from my face to the paper and back.

"Oh, my goodness! This is you!"

"Yeah," I grinned. "I guess you didn't recognize me out of uniform, huh?"

"Yeah, well, also you've got your cowboy hat on. Ha!"

We both laughed.

The man behind me coughed, signaling his exasperation at waiting in line.

"Thanks," I called, busting out of the store.

I ran to my truck, hopped up and down beside the door, then drove home, with a grin that made my face ache.

Over the weeks and months that followed I received hundreds of cards and letters. Some people even sent money. I used their donations to develop a special fund for the dying patients. One patient got a train trip to Pittsburgh to see his daughter before he died.

The response was overwhelming. I guess it's because readers are writers.

A year later, things had settled down, and I was working harder than ever at helping dying persons help themselves. I got paged for an outside call.

"Hello, is this Ufema?"

"Yes," I said, pleasantly surprised that the caller pronounced my name accurately.

"This is Suzanne Saint Pierre, from 60 Minutes."

"Yes," I whispered.

"I'm one of the producers," she explained, "and we're looking to do a piece on death and dying."

"I see," I whispered.

"What? I can't hear you."

"Yes, I see," more audibly.

"I wanted to ask if you're still doing the work that was published about you in *The Washington Post.*"

"As a matter of fact, Miss Saint Pierre, I am."

"I'd like to come to Pennsylvania next week and discuss the possibility of filming you at Harrisburg Hospital."

"That would be great, thank you."

We met the following week. She was very interested in my work and eager to begin production.

"Would it be possible for me to see a few of your patients?" she asked. "I certainly want to respect their privacy, but we also need to tell your story."

"Sure thing. I'm currently working with eleven terminally-ill persons. Why don't we just visit each one and ask how they would feel about being on television. I don't believe in second-guessing anyone," I said emphatically.

As we made the rounds I was pleased by Miss Saint Pierre's poise and gentleness. I told her so.

"Thank you, Joy, why don't you call me Suzanne?"

By the end of the afternoon we had five patients who agreed to be filmed on Monday. Things were moving along, and I was allowing myself to feel excited.

I invited Suzanne to my home for Sunday dinner. Sensing that she was relaxed from work, I asked who would be conducting the interview.

"Oh, gosh," she said sympathetically, "all this time, and I haven't told you?"

"No," I smiled nervously.

"It will be Morley Safer."

"Whew, what a relief! I was worried that it might be Mike Wallace!"

We both laughed.

I arrived at the hospital an hour before the film crew. Eagerness mixed with a bit of anxiety as I bounced up the steps to make final confirmation with the five patients.

I entered the room of the first patient to find her comatose and hours away from death.

The next patient had died late Friday night.

The third candidate said that she had thought about it and changed her mind.

"I've only got two more," I mumbled as I got on the elevator.

The tenth floor was hectic already. Physicians, nurses, and technicians crowded the corridor and station. It took a moment for me to realize that things were a bit too busy for 7:15 a.m. and that most of the commotion was originating from room 1012 where one of my two remaining patients was.

"Oh no," I groaned.

Sure enough, the Italian gentleman with pancreatic cancer who was quite articulate about his feelings of being terminally ill lay dead.

"Oh gosh, Vikki, what happened?" I grabbed one of the nurses.

"Nobody is sure yet, but we think he threw a clot. It's sad, huh?"

"Yes, it is," I said sincerely.

My last hope was in room 1024. I entered and was relieved to see the patient sitting up in bed, eating breakfast.

"Hi, Mim, how are you today?" I inquired.

"Oh, much better! I'm a lot better! In fact, the pain is gone," she replied cheerfully.

"I'm glad. I just stopped by ..."

"In fact," she interrupted, "I think the cancer is gone, too!"

She had been diagnosed two years prior with a nasty type of ovarian carcinoma. What was once a belly full of ascites, or fluid, had become, in the last month, solid tumor.

"Honest, Joy, I've improved so much these past two days, I'm planning to go home by Thursday. It's my youngest boy's birthday. He'll be twelve."

Her eyes couldn't meet mine.

I sat on the side of her bed and held her hand tightly.

"Mim, it's okay if you don't want to do this 60 Minutes thing, honest. I still like and care very much about you."

"Oh, it isn't that at all. I really am much better! You've been so good to me, I wish I could pay you back by doing this TV show for you."

"Mim, you don't owe me a thing. Please don't feel obligated in any way. Just make the most out of the rest of your life, no matter how long or short that might be."

She was crying softly.

I felt a very familiar lump rise in my throat.

"Anyway," she said, wiping her eyes, "I'm needed at home to get this party ready for my Birthday Boy! I can't sit around this dumb old hospital talking about dying."

"You got it, Mim. I must skoot now, but I'll check on you later."

"Fine, Joy, thanks anyway. No hard feelings?"

"No hard feelings."

I kissed her forehead and left.

Back in my office I sat recalling the many patients and families with whom I had worked. Any one of them would be a good teacher, through the camera, to reach others. They had died too soon.

Needing a few laughs, I was on my way to M-4 to have a cup of tea with my old nurse-buddy, Flo.

Opening the door to the stairs, I literally ran into Dr. Royer, one of the oncologists.

"Whoops! Oh, excuse me, Dr. Royer." I apologized.

"That's okay, Joy. I'm glad I bumped into you, ha, ha, a little joke, no?"

"Ha, yes, why did you want to see me?"

"I've got a patient I think you might help. She's a very nice lady with chronic myelogenous leukemia that has turned acute. Her bone marrow is just not producing anymore and even the drugs have failed. She's a lovely person. I'm sure you'll like her."

"Thanks, Dr. Royer, I'm sure I will, too. I'll go see her now."

On my way over to C building, I wasn't sure about visiting this patient so soon after she had received her death sentence. There is such a fine line between allowing an individual time for absorption of bad news and waiting too long till they become so depressed they see no benefit in communication. I decided to trust my sensitivity.

She was propped up in bed, reading her Bible. She had a little flowered cap on to cover her hair loss. A plastic bag hung over the headboard, dripping life-prolonging blood into a vein in her left arm. She smiled weakly. Her face was so pale I could barely discern her lips.

"Mrs. Miller, my name is Joy. I wonder if you feel like chatting about how things are going for you?"

"Oh, yes, Joy, Dr. Royer said that I might be expecting you. Please pull up a chair."

"I don't mind telling you I feel like the angel of death coming in here like this. It's really not that way at all. I just want to be available to you, anytime, in case you feel like talking, about anything."

"Even dying?" she asked, seriously.

"Especially about dying," I answered.

We talked for about twenty minutes, and then I was paged.

"Oh, shoot," I said, "I forgot about them!"

"If you have to go, Joy, it's okay. I'm not going anywhere, at least not yet. Come back when you can."

I explained about the film crew and Morley Safer and 60 Minutes.

"Wow," she said, "I didn't know I was going to meet up with a celebrity!"

"Oh, Marilyn, it's nothing like that. In fact, I don't think they're going to be able to do it now."

"Why not?" she asked.

"I don't have a patient for them to interview."

"What kind of interview?" She removed her glasses and readjusted her cap.

"About dying and how it feels."

"Well, we've been talking about that ever since we met," she laughed.

"Yeah, I don't suppose you would appreciate my timing if I

came in here and asked you to be on 60 Minutes." I sort of giggled.

"Sure I would," she almost beamed.

"You would?" I asked, unbelievingly.

"Sure, when do you want to do it?"

"Today. I mean, ah, this afternoon. Morley Safer is due in at two. Do you really mean it?

"Yes, go get those people and let's get on with it. I'm not going to be around forever, you know."

"Yes, Marilyn, I know. Thanks very much."

The filming went well; in fact, it was probably the best interview I had ever experienced with a patient. She shared her deepest feelings about God and leaving her family. She regretted especially missing out on the children's proms, graduations, and weddings.

She wept, so did I, and so did Suzanne. The film crew stared at the floor and Morley Safer smoked too many cigarettes.

It aired in January and was a grand success. I was very pleased and quite honored. I continued the work that I loved.

A few weeks later it snowed. I had gone into the house to get my .22 caliber revolver for the explicit purpose of shooting the tractor. With a driveway one-half of a mile long, with twelve inches of snow obstructing my departure, I was interested in plowing. After spending over an hour attempting to get the damned thing to start, I returned to the warmth of the house. Struggling to remove my high boots, I fell down in the doorway. As if mocking my predicament, the phone began ringing. Hopping and tripping, I stumbled to the kitchen.

"Yes!" I bellowed into the receiver.

"Hello!" the crackle of long-distance.

"Yes! Hello!"

"Is this Joy Ufema?"

"Yes." Exasperated, dripping snow onto the floor.

"I don't mean to bother you on a Sunday, but ..."

"Then why are you?"

"What? What did you say?"

"Nothing. Who is this?"

"This is Linda Lavin."

"Sure it is!" I replied sarcastically. I had received a few crank calls after 60 Minutes as well as some strange letters. I just wasn't in the mood.

"Joy, honestly, this is Linda Lavin. I just watched a video-tape of your segment on 60 Minutes. I think it's wonderful, and I want to talk with you about doing a movie for CBS."

"I'm not sure what you mean."

"Well, it would be a movie made for television. We'd find a writer to create the script, and I would play you."

"Wow, that sounds fantastic! Tell me more!" I was finally believing.

Linda was very warm and personable. We talked for close to an hour discussing contracts, consultantships, and a tentative date for her to visit me and actually observe my work.

I shared the good news with a few close friends. Later that month, after signing a contract with Lorimar Productions, I shouted to the rooftops.

The whole thing was very exciting, and I was proud, not only of my hard work, but the value all this might bring to dying individuals throughout the country.

We worked laboriously for two years on a script that was acceptable to both Linda and myself. I flew to California for one week to observe part of the filming. It was all very exciting, and everyone was quite gracious, but I found myself eager to return to York County and my simple life on a little farm. Sitting in the middle of MGM studios, surrounded by famous show people, I missed my horse.

The night of the debut of the movie, I gathered a few close friends in my living room. Beside a cozy fire, we sipped champagne and nervously joked. At last, the hour arrived and we sat huddled in front of the TV. Since I had not previewed the film, I was a bit agitated. As it evolved, I saw things on the screen that were not in the script and vice versa. Overall, it seemed fairly good. I felt pleased but disappointed. For the sake of brevity, three characters were combined into one. Fiction wove foreignly into truth. Hollywood had done its Thing.

I was grateful, however, that my story was told. Not many individuals receive recognition for simply doing their job, but I realized, once again, that no matter how we glamorize it or romanticize it, death is an extremely difficult experience.

I watched the screen as a woman acted out her interpretation of what it might be like to be Joy Ufema and work daily, for ten years, with dying individuals. Although death is exhausting with which to wrestle, the "burnout," if there is such a thing, comes from the battle to convince families, staff, clergy, and anyone else coming down the pike, that the worst thing about dying is when the individual is faced with realizing his incompleteness. It is at this time that all his pains exacerbate. His physical pain worsens, and he requires more morphine. His spiritual pain heightens, and he seeks a merciful God. His psychological pain becomes more severe, and he escapes into depression. His socio-logical pain worsens as his family and friends withdraw in pre-paratory grieving, and his financial pain escalates so he curls up to die today instead of next week when he would incur a larger hospital bill.

These pains are too infrequently recognized and acknowl-edged by care-givers, let alone producers and directors.

I, too, get tired and forget. Thanatology is hard work.

I sat at Marilyn's bedside after hanging a plastic bag of rich, red blood.

We both watched as it dripped slowly and steadily through the tubing and into her vein.

"How long is this going to take?" she asked.

"Gosh, Marilyn, you've had hundreds of transfusions. You know, about an hour."

"No, I mean how long is it going to take for me to die?" She looked me square in the eye.

"I would think about six weeks," I answered honestly.

"Then this is the last transfusion I'm going to have. You can't live on someone else's blood forever."

I couldn't speak and didn't want to.

The following morning I was bathing her bruised body. My suntanned hands made such a contrast to her pale skin.

She began to weep.

"Oh, Joy, this is the first time in my life that someone else has had to bathe me. I'm so terribly weak, it's really okay for this to be over soon."

"Is it important to you where your death takes place? Here in the hospital or at home?"

"No," she said, "wherever it happens will be okay. You know Elaine took this year off from college to care for me?"

"Yep. That's a darn good girl you've got, Marilyn."

"Well, this is the end of May, so I figured, if I died soon, the funeral and everything would be finished up this summer, and Elaine could have a little time to get organized in August, then resume her college work in September."

She had it all planned.

She was discharged and remained home till June 5th.

I once more sat by her bed. There would be no transfusion.

"I'm ready to die," she said peacefully.

"If you're asking for permission, you have mine," I said sincerely. "What about that husband of yours and the children?"

"He says he doesn't want me to go, but he can understand how I'm just too tired to fight anymore."

"We'll all be with you," I promised.

It didn't seem to matter, one way or another.

For three days we were her companions. Her family doted, high school chums giggled her into a coma about riding around in an old Ford, each chipping in 30¢ for gasoline, and I read her the Psalms.

On June 9th, she seemed to slip even more. I called her daughter.

"Elaine, this is Joy. I was wondering what time you were planning on coming into the hospital?"

"I'm not," she replied.

"Well, your mother is very much worse, and I thought maybe you'd want to be with her."

"I've decided I don't want to be with her when she dies."

Silence.

"I see."

Silence

"Ah, listen, Elaine, it's really none of my business, but I feel I must share with you some of my experience about this."

"I already know what you're going to say — about being guilty and all that."

"Yes, I am. Those feelings are very real and I've seen many people run into a lot of difficulty dealing with their grief when they are consumed by guilt."

I wanted her there and felt she *should* be there.

"I've thought it all through, and I'm going to feel okay about this," she announced firmly.

"Are you sure, Elaine, because after your mother dies it'll be too late to make this up to her."

"I'm sure."

I returned to Marilyn's room, feeling cheated for her. I stayed late into the evening, hoping Marilyn would soon die.

Early the next morning I again sat by her bed. Hourly she got worse, if that could be, without dying. She was bleeding now, from every orifice. Mucus collecting in her lungs and trachea caused the death rattle to echo through her room and out into the corridor.

I was tired.

I was sick and tired of it.

I told her goodbye and walked away.

As I drove home I realized I had no right to dictate my wishes to Elaine. I finally understood that it's okay to have had enough. The important thing is to be honest about it.

Marilyn died at 2:15 a.m.

Her *entire* family was with her.

VIOLETS

THIS CHAPTER IS ABOUT TWO WOMEN, BOTH OF WHOM WERE named Violet. Although vastly different, they each were very special to me in unique ways.

Violet number one is representative of the problem patient. Nothing is ever acceptable and everything is inadequate. I saw a lot of anger pent up in a sad little lady who saw illness and death as her only recourse in her troubled life.

The referral came from her physician who was a personal friend of mine.

"She's just crazy as hell, Joy. I'm trying to get the psychiatric folks to label her incompetent, then I can have her daughter sign permission for the amputation."

"What kind of amputation?" I inquired.

"Right leg, below the knee. She's got a diabetic ulcer that she just plain neglected. Now the damn thing is gangrenous and has to come off or she'll die. I can't talk any sense into her. That's why I called you. Go in there and convince her she's got to have the amputation."

"Whoa, just a minute, Bill. I don't work that way. What does the patient want?"

"She's crazy. She's not able to make a rational decision."

"Well, how does she feel about having her leg amputated?"

"She doesn't want to. She says she's not going to do it even if it means dying."

"That kind of thinking doesn't seem all that crazy to me. You might even feel the same way."

"I'd never have got myself in that condition, I'll tell you that!"

"Maybe that's where we ought to begin with her. Why did she deliberately ignore the ulcer?"

"Hell, I don't know. That's your job to find out." He marched off, but called over his shoulder, "Let me know soon."

As I neared her room, I saw a student nurse exit in tears, followed by a bedpan sailing through the air, which was blue with language that only Marines use.

Gazing in at her, I couldn't believe my eyes or my nose. She was only five feet tall! How could this little Italian lady cause such a furor? And from where did she get the energy?

I went in to see her.

"What do you want? I suppose they sent you in here to soothe the savage beast?"

"Well, yes, Violet, they did." And so we talked. "I'm here to listen while you talk about your feelings."

"You're no psychiatrist; why would I tell you anything? Are you a priest?"

I just couldn't get to her. Every day I'd go in and try, and she just wouldn't allow me to get close.

"Is that your paycheck sticking out of your pocket?"

"Yes, Violet."

"Oh, God, you mean you get paid to come in and harass people like me? Do you sleep all right at night with that kind of guilt?"

"Violet, I'm here simply because I care about you. I'm interested in . . ." Suddenly my pager beeped. "Violet, may I use your telephone, please?"

"Of course, you'd use it anyway. Just put a dime by it."

It was Suzanne Saint Pierre from 60 Minutes. "Oh, yes, hi, Suzanne. Do you have a date for me?"

Violet said, "Go on your lousy date and leave me here to rot. You're just like all the other ones. Caring, caring, caring."

"Excuse me, Suzanne. Violet, this is not that kind of date. Listen, Suzanne, this is not a good time to talk. I'll try and call you back. Just see if you can get the date. Now, listen, Violet, it was not that kind of date. What I wanted to tell you is, have you ever watched 60 Minutes at all?"

"Oh yes, I kept it on for 60 seconds and then turned it off."

"Well, anyway, they did a piece about my work here with dying patients, and the date I was inquiring about was to see when they were going to air it."

She sat quietly, intently staring at me. Hands folded tightly on her lap, her dark brown eyes bore through me.

I said nothing.

She said, "Oh, Joyce, why do you lie like that?"

"It's true, Violet, I'm going to be on 60 Minutes. What do you think?"

Silence. With a wave of her hand, she dismissed me.

Two weeks later I told her the date in January when my story would appear.

"*Maybe* I'll watch it." she said, curtly. "*If* I'm even alive."

"What do you mean?"

"Don't play dumb with me! You know all about it."

"I honestly don't know what you're talking about, Violet."

"The nursing home!" she spit the words out venomously. "I'm going to Penfield Nursing Home — to wait to die. Ha! What do you think of that, Miss Joyce?!"

Suddenly I realized it all clearly. Through the swearing and shouting, the caustic, volatile behavior, I heard fear.

I sat down on her bed (she did not move over to make room) and gently took her hand. She roughly pulled away. I took it again. She pulled away. I took it again. She held.

"Violet, even though you say you don't believe me, I have supported your decision not to have your leg amputated. And I've gone to bat for you against all your doctors and lots of these nurses."

She sat quietly.

"We may not get another opportunity to share again. For the last time, Violet, would you tell me why?"

"Why what?"

"Why you didn't see a doctor a year ago, when your ulcer first began?"

"It's simple . . . I hate him."

"Hate who? Your doctor?"

"No, stupid. My husband. I hate my husband."

Taken a bit by surprise, I was momentarily speechless.

"What's the matter?" she asked sarcastically. "Cat got your tongue? You've been buggin' me all this time, and when I finally tell you, you can't think of anything brilliant to say. You're a good one, all right."

"Why do you hate him?" I gently asked.

"Because he had that Goddamned stroke and I have to take care of him all the time! That's why!"

"Do you think maybe you consciously held off going to the doctor for yourself so that your leg would get so bad that you couldn't possibly continue to care for him?"

"There you go with that psychiatric crap again."

"I just want you to know you have other options besides dying."

"Yeah, like what? Like flying to the moon?"

"Violet, you're only 52 years old, and you don't need to go back to your husband. You can divorce him and we can cut off that lower part of your leg and give you a prothesis and you can move to New York and do whatever you want to do."

Just for a couple of seconds, I had her. She started to cry for a minute about the desperateness and how as a Catholic, she couldn't do it. And there was no option for her. I reached over to wipe a tear.

"Don't touch me! Why don't you just leave me alone?"

"Because I genuinely care."

"Well, I don't need you to care. Obviously, you're the one who needs the shrink. You're all screwed up because you need to be needed. Well, go find someone out there who wants your care and leave me alone!"

She rolled over on her side facing away.

That afternoon she was discharged to Penfield Nursing Home. Months later, after horrendous pain, the gangrenous leg rotted through the bone and actually fell off. She died a few days later, a week before Christmas.

The grief I felt was not over a dying human being, it was for a woman who had never lived. She allowed her existence to be controlled by "shoulds," demands she thought would satisfy her family and her God. But what about her responsibility to herself? Was the suffering she inflicted self-induced as a penance for feeling guilty for wanting something else from life?

If she would have said yes to her own heart, she wouldn't have said no to so many other hearts.

The second Violet I will share with you had an entirely different personality. The lesson I learned from her was no better than from Violet number one, just different.

I ran up seven flights of stairs. Emerging through the door of the tenth floor, I tried to appear calm. (Difficult, to say the least, when one is both out of shape and out of breath.) As cool as I could, I confidently strolled behind the nurses' station to find Mrs. Graham's chart.

Moments earlier, I had been paged by the ward secretary who told me that Mrs. Graham's surgeon had actually referred her to me. My excitement over receiving my very first referral from a prominent surgeon betrayed me through a big grin as I eagerly reached for the chart. Leafing through the many pages, I finally came upon the physician's order sheet. Rapidly scanning the many pages, I finally sighted the lusted-for statement. Unfortunately, it wasn't quite the justifiable celebration I had hoped. The order simply read "death and destruction squad may see this patient." Somehow it all seemed anticlimatic. Anyway, I wiped a crumb of humble pie from my face and walked into the patient's room. She was a lovely young woman, extremely ill, receiving intravenous fluids, and holding an emesis basin under her chin. I must confess that my thoughts were not on listening well to what Mrs. Graham was saying. I was also fantasizing about writing a prophetic account of this interview on the impressive pink consultation sheet complete with two carbons. Since this was the genesis of my referral career, I was eager to impress the surgeon. After all, if he was pleased with my help for this particular patient, then perhaps he would seek my expertise for future dying patients. I felt elated over the potential breakthrough.

After approximately fifteen minutes of talking "at" Vi, I

excused myself and went to the desk to begin my essay-report. The words wouldn't come because what I was attempting to transfer from my head to paper wasn't real. I was too caught up in trying to impress. Recognizing my mistake, I threw the pink consultation sheet in the waste can, then returned to Vi's bedside. I quickly related my error with her, and she even managed a weak chuckle. Then I got down to work. I gave Vi the undivided attention I had prided myself on giving almost all of my patients. Once again, she spoke, but this time I listened well.

She was about 46, had cancer of the ovaries, with gross metastiasis throughout her pelvis. She also had a lot of fluid in her belly with great pain. Wasted and frail, receiving I.V. for vomiting, she was just grossly ill, and requiring morphine around the clock in this little 100-pound body. So I really got down to brass tacks with her, and just simply said:

"Violet, what do you want now?"

And she said, "I want to go home."

It's important to clarify with patients their specific terminology. Sometimes home means Heaven.

So I said, "You mean home to die?"

And she said, "Yes."

And maybe she could have said, "No, I just want to get my strength back." And so I would have tempered the conversation accordingly.

No, it was home to die, she understood all that. I said, "I want you to know that if you go home now, I think you will die sooner than if you would stay here with the I.V.'s and all that."

She said she understood, but she really had to hurry and get home.

I said, "Okay, how does Jack (her husband) feel about that?" She said they'd briefly discussed it, and he was amenable to it, although they both had some fears. So I called him and shared with him our conversation.

They had a grocery store in Holidaysburg, just a small town. He said he'd get somebody in to run the store or he'd close it, but he was going to take Vi home for the remainder of her life. And I assured him that I thought it would not be very long at all, that she was hanging on so she could die in her own bed. It was springtime, so I took a couple of days working with Jack, teaching him how to give her morphine injections (this was before Brompton's mix was popular—she was vomiting and couldn't keep oral drugs down anyway). He'd get an orange and practice. We got her a hospital bed and sent her home. At the nurses' residence, they had daffodils growing outside, so I stole a bouquet of those for her, got her in the ambulance, and kissed her goodbye, with my finger crossed that she would live that long (but I think we *do* what we *need* to do). She got home, and Jack was there caring for her. We got a wonderful visiting nurse in.

About four or five days later, I called to check on them because the weekend was coming up.

"Hi, Jack, this is Joy, how's it going?"

He said, "Pretty good, I made her some vegetable soup. She liked it, and she kept it down."

Remember she'd been vomiting so we couldn't keep even tea or jello and I.V.'s and all that down. And so it started clicking, what's the difference here? Well, *homemade* vegetable soup, *Jack* made it.

I said, "Okay, Jack, that's good. Now listen, why I'm calling, too, is I have another prescription for you for that morphine, the pain shot stuff."

He said, "Yes, in that brown bottle."

"That's right, Jack, you know the weekend's coming up, and I don't want Vi to be in pain at all, so I got another prescription for you, just in case you were going to run out. We used a lot in the hospital, you know, every two hours."

He said, "I didn't give her any of that yet."

And I said, "Oh."

Then he said, "Well, you know that hospital bed you got us?"

"Yes."

"Well, I don't have her in that."

I said, "That's okay, Jack, where do you have her?"

He said, "She's in our bed."

I said, "Well, that's fine if she's comfortable there. But you're doing a lot of the 24-hour care, and I'm worried about your rest. So where are you sleeping?"

He said, "I'm sleeping in our bed, too."

"Are you hugging that girl?"

"Yes." And that's why she didn't need any morphine, and that's why the vegetable soup stayed down. The difference of being in our own home, our own bed, our own surroundings.

I said, "Okay, Jack, that's super."

I was to see Vi on Monday, but Sunday at about ten in the morning, he called and said, "It's all over—she just went to sleep and died." And he said her sister was with her and the dog was lying in the bedroom on the rug, you know. The physician had been there, and he said he didn't think it was long, and she just slept away.

It was spring, and he said, "I had her out in the garden yesterday, Joy, in her wheelchair, and this was twelve hours before her death, you know. She really talked a lot about the resurrection of the earth and the whole cycle of spring, and the resurrection of the body, you know, and I think it was okay for her. You know it really hurt me to watch her wither and die, but I found out what my Violet wanted, and I did it for her, didn't I?"

I replied, "You sure did, Jack."

I called him 30 days later, on the anniversary of her death. The phone rang and rang. I was briefly worried, and finally he answered.

I said, "Jack, this is Joy, and I know what day today is, and I was wondering how you are doing. It took you a long time to answer the phone. I wondered if you had left or something."

"Oh, no," he said, "I'm not going to leave, but I'm packing. I'm going to Oregon, hunting and fishing for the summer with my brother."

Jack is okay. He is not sitting in the living room, reclusively going over old pictures of Vi. And he's not up at the Holidaysburg Cemetery, mumbling something into her tombstone about being sorry that she died in the nursing home because he just "couldn't do it." Jack is okay. He lost weight, and he lost sleep. Worst of all, he lost his darling Violet. But he risked asking Vi what she wanted, and he did it for her.

WHAT IS YOUR SONG AND
WHY AREN'T YOU SINGING IT?

I HAD BEEN WORKING AS THE "NURSE-SPECIALIST IN DEATH AND dying" for about one year. Since Harrisburg Hospital was a teaching hospital, training nurses and physicians, there were frequent opportunities to attend lectures by reknowned guest speakers. On one particular occasion I went to a conference presented by Dr. Klaus Bauhnson from Eastern Pennsylvania Psychiatric Institute. Taking frantic notes, I was amazed at the content of his discourse. He was a physician, specialising in psychiatry, and researching the personality profile of the cancer patient. He also identified specific target organs a certain type of personality would choose for their cancer. His message was enthralling, applause was sparce, and I was eager for more.

Over the next few years I would dabble a bit at applying his observations to a dozen or so select patients. I was gentle but not timid. I referred a young man with cancer of the testicles to Dr. Bauhnson. He saved his life through psychotherapy.

As I continued my work, I sense the truth of the premise that emotions not discharged will have a physical effect on the body. I began, in a mild manner, simply inquiring from my patients why they felt a need to be ill at this time. The question held no judgment. Patients were neither offended nor surprised. Repeatedly, a pattern of stress-related illness unfolded. And, then, I asked, "Do you need to die?" The answer, several hundred times was yes. Patients confessed they never really had the spark of life very long. When their lives were relatively happy, they told themselves this is too good to be true, it can't last, and it didn't. The self-fulfilling prophecy came true, they lost their spouse, job or hope, and within two weeks to eighteen months they were diagnosed with a malignancy.

The majority of my patients were women with breast cancer. They all died. I had attended too many of their funerals and heard too many of their best friends say, "It's really too bad about Miriam. She'd do anything for anybody."

"Yes," I thought, "she had to die just to be free to say no."

Throughout the next year I became more aware of other professionals sharing this philosophy. Galen, the Greek physician, stated in 200 A.D., "Depressed women get breast cancer, not happy women."

Larry LeShan, a psychologist from New York was quoted in the *Washington Star*, "If you feel good about yourself, you will not only fight cancer, you will not be inclined to get it in the first place."

He cites classic characteristics: an inability to become aggressive in the person's own defense, and despair — not only for what the individual has done, but over the fact that they felt they had done nothing. The diagnosis of cancer does not cause their despair, says Dr. LeShan. The cancer only confirms the hopelessness they have felt.

"Part of the treatment is to turn this sweetheart into an assertive, scrappy individual," says Carl Simonton, M.D., in his book *Getting Well Again*.

He says it is imperative to include the patient's family in the remolding. After all, the husband slouched in front of his television bellowing out an order to his wife to "gimme another beer" is not likely to be pleased with the metamorphosis that occurred to her from therapy when, for the first time in 22 years, she replies with, "Get it yourself, I'm busy."

This kind of change of personality is hard work, and risky. What if the patient's spouse refuses to participate in therapy? What if the spouse likes things just the way they are even though their marriage partner has been diagnosed with cancer? I referred a young man with lymphoma to Dr. Bauhnson. He wasn't sure he wanted to put so much energy into changing himself, even though, he admitted, it would probably be for the better.

"I believe in this theory, Tim, and I believe if you don't jump right into it, you're going to die."

"Yeah, I know, Joy. I prefer to die."

And he did. But not Mike.

I was making rounds with the oncologists one afternoon when we entered the room of an 18 year old diagnosed with lympho-sarcoma. After assisting with a bone marrow aspiration, I sat with the young man. Our conversation was easy, nothing too deep or heavy, then I left. The following morning I found a note taped on the door to my office. It was from Mike, requesting another visit.

Removing a copy of Mad Magazine, I sat on the side of his bed. He looked good. His blue eyes were bright and he smiled a lot.

"Mike," I began, "I want to set the record straight, right from the start, you're not dying."

"Yeah," he grinned, "I know that."

"Okay, so what's so urgent that you forced yourself down three flights of steps to personally deliver this note?"

"Well, I thought maybe we could talk about me having cancer and some ideas I have about why and stuff like that."

"Yes, indeed, I'd be very interested in those thoughts."

"Well," he sighed, "I think it began about a year ago, when my parents got a divorce. I seemed to be the one that took it the hardest. My twin sister wasn't too upset or my older brother. It was like I would have to be the man of the family now."

"What about your brother? Isn't he the oldest?"

"Yeah, but he's a bum. He's 23 and still lives at home and everything."

"Does he work anywhere?"

"No, he had a job, but they fired him. It's been pretty tough financially as well as emotionally, and I've always been the one who feels the effects the most. I guess I'm sorta sensitive," he said, looking down.

"Mike, how do you think all that you've told me fits in with being diagnosed with cancer?"

"See, I didn't know for sure it was going to be cancer, but I sure knew if I got sick, real sick, I mean, that my family would see that I just couldn't do everything for everybody any more and they'd have to start doing stuff for themselves."

"Did you also hope that by being real sick your parents might reconcile their differences and repair their marriage?"

"Yeah, I wanted them to call off the divorce."

"Have they?"

"No."

I reached for his hand at the same moment he reached for mine.

He began again. "Do you know that I have 'Stage II A Lymphoblastic Lymphophosarcoma'?"

Pleased that his physician had been totally honest with him, I said, "Yes, I know."

"Then you also must know that Stage II is a lot better than Stage IV. Right?"

He eagerly awaited my confirmation.

"Damned right," I said emphatically. "What are you saying, Mike?"

"Well, maybe I got cancer not bad enough to die, but just bad enough to let them know I just can't take it any more."

He covered his face and began to cry.

"Mike, I'd like us to be friends, no matter what happens with you, and I want you to know I'll always be honest with you, about everything."

He blew his nose, then smiled.

"Good," he said.

He listened attentively for the next half hour as I explained the theory of stress-related cancer. He became excited over learning that if a person has responsibility for getting diseased, he can also have responsibility for curing it.

"What does this Dr. LeShan say I would have to do?" he asked.

"I think he'd have you begin with feeling good enough about yourself to be assertive with your family regarding your rights. Instead of having to get sick and manipulating their behavior, work at being honest and open about your feelings."

"Yeah," he said, with a gleam in his eye, "I'm ready."

Over the next few months I received several phone calls from Mike. He would report that his life was going well and that his new approach was effective.

He suffered occasional setbacks. Still living at home and working for a local insurance firm, he was exposed to periodic attacks of irresponsibility by his siblings. His mother would not take over her parental role, and Mark would feel guilty for not bailing things out and soothing everyone's wounds at his own expense, as he had done in the past.

Inevitably, his lymph glands would become swollen and sore and he would require brief hospitalization. During one of his stays, I confronted him.

"Well, old buddy, what do you think is going on?" I sank into a lounge chair and poured each of us a glass of ginger ale.

"I don't know. Sometimes it's hard to be strong and not give in to them."

"Your family?" I clarified.

"Yeah."

"Mike, I talked with Dr. Boreman, and he says you're doing real well. In fact, he'd like to stop chemotherapy. Frankly, I'm worried that all your symptoms could return unless you really stick to your guns with your family."

"I know what you mean."

"I have an idea. How would you feel about moving away from home?"

He sat quietly.

"To tell you the truth, I've been considering it. In fact, I was going to surprise you later, but I guess you might as well know now."

"What? I know! You're getting married!"

"No, silly. I've applied to go to college at Penn State."

"Fantastic! What would be your major?"

"Business Administration."

"It's what you've been interested in for years, huh?"

"Yeah," he grinned.

I gave him a big hug, spilling the ginger ale. We both laughed.

He became serious once more. "Joy, will my family really be okay without me?"

"Mike, it isn't all or none. You're not deserting them. You're just going to be living your own life now. You can still be supportive and certainly continue loving them, but you're just not going to sacrifice your life, literally, for them."

"Okay," he said. "I feel really good about all this."

"Great, So do I."

He left in the fall and excelled in his studies. The last I saw of him was Christmas of his senior year. He was lifting weights and was a valuable member of the track team. He had required no chemotherapy for five years. Dr Boreman still refers to him as his cure boy. I refer to him as a very brave human being who knew what his song was and finally drew, from deep inside, the courage to sing it.

I don't think I need to point out the lesson to be learned here.

LET'S PRETEND THIS WILL GO AWAY

I WAS LIFTING THE PATIENT FROM A LITTER TO HER BED WHEN she vomited feces on me. After cleaning her up, I sat on her bed and asked what she wanted now — now that things were getting serious.

"I don't need to talk about this," she said. "I worked as a nurses' aid at Polyclinic Hospital. I've seen a lot of patients as sick as I am and they got better."

She continued to utilize gross denial even though her condition deteriorated rapidly. She had a tumor throughout her large intestine, causing total obstruction and stool in her vomit. I've never seen a patient live longer than 24 hours with these symptoms.

"Is there anything important you need me to help you do?"

"No, just as soon as I get my strength back, I'm going to return to work."

Her blatant denial was frustrating. I fantasized that she might miss out on many unfinished items in her life. She never shared much with me, the nursing staff, or her family. We all agreed on a mutual goal — to be available and willing to listen if and when she *chose* to share. The use of denial was very necessary to her and she had the right to utilize it for as long as she needed to.

The head nurse on day shift made early rounds and found Mrs. Waters dead. While assisting with her postmortem care, I found the following note in her drawer:

For my burial, put me in the pink nightie that Barbara got me that I saved and never wore. No flowers. Have people

sing my favorite hymn, 'Beneath the cross of Jesus'. Don't
make no big fuss.

How ironic. Obviously, Mrs. Waters knew exactly how seriously ill she was and, for a few moments, stood toe-to-toe with
death, long enough to specify a few simple wishes.

My involvement with this patient was quite a learning experience. My genuine concern to do what was best for her coupled
with frustration led me to Elisabeth Kubler-Ross.

She was scheduled to present a conference at one of the
colleges in central Pennsylvania. I had the honor of meeting her
at the airport and sharing dinner with her in my home prior to
her scheduled appearance.

We had chatted together over the years, so I felt comfortable
in expressing my difficulty in knowing the best approach with
Mrs. Waters.

Riding along, Elisabeth searched through my car for an ashtray. I was rambling on, presenting my patient, anxious to find
the perfect answer from *the* great mentor. Finally discovering the
elusive ashtray, Elisabeth flipped it open to discover it was full of
quarters, nickels, and dimes.

"Now where in Heaven's name am I supposed to put this
cigarette?" she asked with a grin.

"I don't care Elisabeth. I've been waiting for weeks to discuss
this very difficult problem with you. Have you been listening?"

"Yes," she said seriously.

"Well, I've read all your books and listened to your tapes, and
I can't find the answer, so I'm very interested in hearing it
directly from you."

"Okay, I will tell you."

I rolled up my window, closed the vent, and leaned sideways,
eager to capture every syllable from the great Kubler-Ross that
would solve this dilemma.

I waited for her response.

She took a long drag on her cigarette.

I began to perspire.

She spoke.

"Joy, when the patient is in denial, she's in denial." That's all she said.

"What?"

"When the patient is in denial, she's in denial," she repeated, patiently and matter-of-factly.

"Elisabeth, I'm well aware of what you say on page 46. I want to know how to handle her well, for her."

"I just told you. Oh, what a quaint, little town this is. What is the name of this place?"

"Huh? Ah, oh, Mechanicsburg."

"Well, Mechanicsburg, you have such quaint, little buildings. So, Joy, tell me about the television interview at 7:00."

The lesson was finished. School was out. She had said her piece, simple enough, and moved on.

I was hoping for something more profound, perhaps more grandiose.

Weeks later I would be impressed by the efficacy of that single statement.

I was on the fourth floor of the hospital—a medical-surgical unit.

"Hey, Nurse, I'm really sorry."

"It's okay, Mr. Snipes," I answered sympathetically as I cleaned bright blood off my white shoes. "I'm very concerned about your health. Vomiting blood is a dangerous sign."

"Naw, I'm okay." He spit blood into a basin, then looked up at me. "See, I'll tell you how this works. I only had about $200 and so my doctor, he just done $200 worth of surgery on me. Next Friday, my brother-in-law is going to loan me another couple hundred, and then my doctor is going to finish the job in there on me."

I was astounded.

"Mr. Snipes, I have to tell you again how worried I am about your health. This bleeding has me concerned. Do you want to talk about anything?"

"Nope, I'm just fine, thanks." He closed his eyes, dismissing me.

I paged Big John, the black orderly, and asked him to please meet me in the snack bar. "You buying?" he teased.

"I guess, but you may only order a coke, nothing else."

A few minutes later we sat talking. I shared my opinion that I felt Mr. Snipes was dying. "The sad part, John, is that he doesn't seem to be comfortable talking about his serious illness. I'm wondering if he's utilizing a true denial or if it's because I'm female or if it's because I'm white."

"Well, it could be both of them last points. How can I help?"

"Thanks for offering. If you could just ask him a few gentle questions and then tell me his responses. We can get a pretty good idea how he's coping."

"Okay, you got a deal."

"It's not for me, John, it's for him."

The next day, I passed by Mr. Snipe's room and saw his bed empty. Inquiring at the nurses' station, I learned he had died at 6 a.m. that morning. I quickly paged John. "No time for a coke. Just hurry, and tell me what happened."

"Well, I took a few minutes last evening and sat down with him. I mean, I had a lot of enemas to give, but I actually sat down with him."

"That's great, John, what happened?" I could hardly contain myself.

"Well, it was real easy. I just sat there and it turned out he knew my Dad ... stuff like that. Then he told me about his wife working over in C Building, in housecleaning. So he had me go get her and bring her here. This was like around 10:30. I left to go help out in the fracture room. Some guy busted his arm in a fight down at Dino's Bar. Man! You ever been there? That place is so ..."

"John! Please tell me what happened!"

"Okay, okay. Like I said, I left for a little bit and when I went back, he was sleeping and his wife was just leaving. She told me he confessed to her that twelve years ago he had an affair with another woman. Then he asked her to forgive him, and she said she did."

"Then what happened?"

"Nothing. He dies in his sleep. Listen, I gotta run. Is there anything else, Joy?"

"Yeah, I owe you a coke."

Again, what had transpired was a witnessing of defense mechanisms in action. Mr. Snipes conjured up a reason that, for the most part, sustained him through the dying process. At some point, however, he had to put that shield down and deal realistically with blatant signs of his body's degeneration.

He did this, as did Mrs. Waters, only when he was ready. Only when it was right for him.

I recall early days, just beginning my work as a nurse-thanatologist. During that initial period, trying to cope with jealous, angry, threatened nurses, I rarely had company during lunch.

Grateful for companionship, I was pleased to slide over when an older nurse, not known for tender, sensitivity, asked to join me.

Sighing loudly, she flopped down, bumping the table leg and spilling my tea.

"Oh, man," she moaned, "I've been doing your death work for you."

A bit amazed, I said, "Oh?"

"Yeah, that guy up in 548 by the door. I've been doing this death stuff you do."

I watched, mesmerized, as she mixed her creamed corn, boiled potatoes, and Hungarian goulash into a large mound on her plate.

"Unfortunately, there are too many patients in need of my service." I said, staring at her tray.

"Well, I've been workin' all morning on that guy in 548 trying to get him to say it."

"Say what?"

"That he's dying. That's what you do, don't ya? You make 'em say it — get them to open up, right?"

She was now pouring salad dressing over the entire concoction on her plate, mixing and stirring.

"Yes, I help patients to open up but I don't use a can opener."

She never did learn sensitivity, and I'm not sure it can even be taught. I am sure, though, that we can develop the skill of sitting down and shutting up. The patient who needs desperately to pretend this is going away is very vulnerable. Even if you could convince him otherwise, and you *can't,* simply because he's not ready, it is cruel to attempt to do so.

Elisabeth Kubler-Ross was right. "When the patient is in denial, they're in denial." I believe if we can remain supportive and nonjudgmental, the patient might work through his fear enough to share. But only when he's ready. We also have to accept that this may never happen, at least as we are aware. And we have to accept that that's okay, because that's how this particular individual wants it. And isn't that really what *we* want for him?

WHAT'S THE WORST THING THAT COULD HAPPEN?

18

PASSING THE INTENSIVE CARE UNIT I HEARD CRYING. UNABLE to continue with a clear conscience, I asked the sobbing woman if I could help.

"I don't think anyone can now; it's too late."

"Why don't you just start at the beginning?" I said.

"Well, it's my husband. The doctor was just here to tell me he has cancer in his lungs. I'm devastated. When he first examined Bill in the office, he said he was sure it was just in one lung, and the surgery would make him all right."

"Did your husband have surgery?"

"Yes, about two hours ago. I thought everything would be okay, but then our doctor just stopped in here and told me he couldn't get any of it." She started crying again. "He said Bill wasn't going to live very long."

I put my arm around her and patted her hand.

"You've been so nice, Dear, would you stop in and see my Bill tomorrow?"

"Of course, I'd be happy to."

"He'll be transferred from Intensive Care out into the main hospital." She started crying again. "I guess when there's nothing more to do for someone, they don't keep them in ICU."

"I promise to stop by and visit your husband tomorrow."

The next day, I went to the medical/surgical floor. His surgeon was standing in the nurses' station. While looking at the patient's chart, I was tapped on the shoulder by the physician.

"Listen, you're not going back there, are you, to talk to Mr. Smith?"

"Yes, as a matter of fact, I am."

"Well, listen, I don't want you back there." We're not going to tell him."

"Well, Doctor, what is the worst thing that could happen here, if we did tell him?"

"He'll die."

"Well, he *is* dying" I said.

"No! You know what I mean. He'll just lay down and give up."

"Yes, that could happen, and even if it does, it's not our fault. It's the patient choosing how he wants to handle this situation. If he wants to curl up and die, that's his right."

"Well, okay, I'll tell you what really could happen. He could go home and shoot his head off, then it'll be your fault because you told him this bad news."

"Well, I would certainly like to think that he wouldn't have to resort to that, that we could offer enough emotional support to get him through this," I replied. "But even if he does, that's still his choice isn't it? And that's how he chooses to handle this stressful situation, and it's his right even if we disagree with it. But he has to have all the information to make his decision." The surgeon left.

I went back. Never having seen this patient before, I sat on his bed and put my hand on his shoulder. I said nothing. He said to me,

"Let's pretend you came in here and just told me that I had three months to live."

I said, "Let's pretend that. What would you do?"

He said, "I have a cabin on the Susquehanna River. I'd go there fishing."

I said, "Do you need any help getting there?"

"No, my brother is taking me next Saturday."

What a lovely conversation between two human beings! Not a nurse and patient or between a thanatologist and a client. This was just a very gentle sharing between one human being who simply must leave a little before the other. It was made possible, though, because both of us had the guts and the integrity to actually address "what is the worst thing that could happen?"

A few weeks later I utilized my new learning in a situation not quite as serious but, nevertheless, just as important.

I had been visiting the patient for only a few minutes, when I, embarrassed, excused myself and gratefully left his room.

I barely made it to the air conditioner at the end of the hall. With great gulps, I breathed in the coldness, relieved at feeling better. A few minutes later, in my office, I held a chastising conversation with myself.

"What's the matter with you?"

"I don't know. I used to pride myself at being able to tolerate all kinds of foul odors."

"Sure, Supernurse, but what are you going to do about this particular situation?"

The patient in discussion was a gentleman with an unusually agressive naso-pharangeal tumor that had invaded the roof of his mouth and up into his nose and sinuses. Externally, his face revealed some distortion, but it was the terrible odor that kept visitors and staff from spending too much time in his room. His wife asked me to speak with him regarding his feelings about being seriously ill. I had made several attempts at doing just that. However, it was close to impossible for me to remain at his bedside for longer than five minutes.

Too vain to admit my humanness, I chose to discuss the situation with a friend. She had no hospital orientation, but offered a most pragmatic idea.

"Why didn't I think of that?" I exclaimed.

The next day, I entered that patient's room. The electric deodorizer and pan of charcoal did nothing to clear the air. Clutched in my hand was a brown paper bag, containing what I prayed would be the answer. Although the task ahead of me was difficult, I bravely marched forward.

"Mr. James, I've been too embarrassed to talk with you about why I don't stay longer during our chats."

"Yeh, well, I figured it was the smell. I mind it too, you know."

He smiled patiently as I continued. "Mr. James, I'm here

because I genuinely care about you. So much that I want to try something that may help me get to know you better."

"Yeh, sure, anything you want," he eagerly agreed.

"Okay, here we go."

I deftly withdrew from the brown bag a brand-name solid-stick air freshener with a lemon label and a 67¢ price tag. "Would you be offended, Mr. James, if I just held this in my hand and occasionally took a whiff?"

"Heck, no, only give me a sniff, too. Now, let's get on with this talking. I got a lot of things to say."

What took place here was answering the question "what is the worst thing that could happen." I probably would make excuses, like everyone else, and not visit Mr. James. He would die, isolated, never having been given the opportunity to share any of his feelings about his horrible disease or impending death or anything! All because I needed to save face. Certainly not acceptable.

The other scarey thing about all this is that he might be terribly offended by me bringing an air freshener along for every visit. Weighing the two choices I decided the worst thing was his isolation, so I took the risk.

I wasn't as lucky the next day. Perhaps I was becoming overconfident in my new-found success. The challenge presented itself. I accepted. It didn't work this time.

The next story I'd like to talk about involves asking "what is the worst thing that could happen" when a conflict can arise between the patient, or, in this particular case, the "consumer" and a physician.

I had always felt a dislike from Dr. Turner ever since I began my work with dying patients. He was a General Practitioner who would respond to patient's inquiries with the comment "Now you don't need to know any of that information. I'm your doctor and I'll tell you what I think you should know."

On numerous occasions his terminal patients were detained from going home simply because they had fever or he was waiting till they "got their strength back."

I went to visit a lovely lady who was a patient of Dr. Turner's. She had been under his care for many years, though dissatisfied.

Now she had been diagnosed with a malignancy.

It was a gentle visit. Not too heavy. I was enjoying chatting when the patient interjected.

"So I told my doctor that if I don't soon get some relief from pain, I'm going to have to do myself in."

"Oh, Nellie, did he give you something to help?"

"Sort of."

"What do you mean, 'sort of'?"

"Well, I want to go home so bad, but he told me he wouldn't give me any prescriptions because he wasn't going to be party to my suicide."

"What are your plans now?" I asked, holding her hand in mine.

"I'm pretty upset about how things are turning out. He said he would give me prescriptions for pain medicine if I would go to a nursing home. That way, the nurses would control the medicine and there wouldn't be any way I could do myself in. He said it would be shots so I couldn't save up pills."

The whole thing was absurb.

"What are you going to do?"

"What can I do? I'm sort of weak but not bed-fast. I just can't stand the pain."

She had cancer of the liver which is notoriously painful. It's a large organ, surrounded by a capsule, so when tumors grow, there is little room for expansion.

"The ambulance is on the way. I signed his papers that I would go to the nursing home. He has other patents there."

"Nellie, what do you want to do?"

"Like I said, I want to go home, to my place, but I'm pretty weak." She certainly looked ill, but not as if she was going to die.

"How would you feel about going to your son's home instead?"

"To Rod's? Oh, I'd love that!"

"Did you ask him how he'd feel about it?"

"No, because my doctor wouldn't give me the prescriptions for pain. I just gotta get some relief."

"I have an idea, Nellie. How would you feel about changing doctors? If Rod would agree to have you live with him, we could get your new doctor to write all the prescriptions you need. What do you think?''

"Oh, Joy, that would be marvelous! But we couldn't possibly get away with it. I already signed those papers and all, and the ambulance is due here any minute.''

"Let me quick make a few phone calls.''

Within moments, I contacted physician friend who agreed to accept Nellie in all the circumstances. He phoned in a prescription to a drug store close to Rod's home. If Nellie went to the Nursing Home instead, the pharmacist would cancel the request. As I was dialing Rod's phone number, the ambulance crew arrived and began lifting Nellie onto the litter.

I said, "No, just wait a minute.'' I quickly identified myself to Rod and asked how he'd feel about caring for his mother.

"We'd love it!'' he said, "How come she never asked?''

"It's a long story so I'll tell you later. I'll make arrangements for everything from this end. Your mother will be there in less than an hour, okay?''

"Okay! We'll roll out the red carpet.''

The crew was pacing. "Hey, Nurse, hurry up. We got other runs to make.''

"Okay, she can go now, but it's not to the Nursing Home. Nellie will give you the right address.''

I called several times and she was doing beautifully. She was fairly free of her pain and gaining strength. About two months later, I called and Rod said, "She's not here anymore.''

My heart paused. "What do you mean, Rod?''

"She's not with us any longer. She moved back to her own apartment. She's doing real good.''

One year later, I sat beside her during a relatively peaceful death. It was in the same room and the same bed where we had pulled the old "Nursing Home switch.''

Dr. Turner never spoke to me again, and he never learned from his patients that death is not the worst thing that can happen, inhumanity is.

FACING FEAR

H E SAT IN A LARGE CHAIR OUTSIDE OF MY OFFICE HOLDING A box of doughnuts on his lap. He knew why he had an appointment with the death and dying nurse — his mother was upset because he refused to enter the bedroom in which his Grandfather lay dying.

I greeted the lad and invited him to sit in my office where we could talk privately. He hopped off the chair adroitly shifting the box of doughnuts from one hand to the other. He seemed poised for a ten year old despite the unrulely blond cowlick standing at the back of his head.

"Should I sit there, Miss Ufema?" he asked, pointing to a chair beside my desk.

"No, Jimmy, let's both sit over here on these chairs. I think we'll be more comfortable."

"It's James."

"What?"

"My name," he said politely. "I prefer being called James."

I pretended to cough to stifle a chuckle, regained my composure then joined him in sitting down.

"James, I want to start off our talk by telling you that I'm not a psychiatrist or a doctor. I'm just your friend. That's why I'm not sitting behind my desk. I prefer being relaxed and easy."

"I understand perfectly well, Miss Ufema, you're trying to tell me that you're not representing a threatening authority figure."

"Yes, that's correct," I pretended to cough again. "By the way," I ressumed, "I prefer being called Joy."

"Very well," he said, "Joy, would you care for a doughnut? I highly recommend the chocolate icing ones."

He opened the box of calorie-oozing, doughy, go-to-your-hips goodies. Suddenly the fruit and yogurt breakfast seemed ridiculous and I eagerly yielded to temptation.

We sat eating doughnuts, smiling and licking our fingers. I gave him warm, safe eye-contact. With difficulty I remained silent. Finally, *he* said,

"My Grandfather is dying, you know."

Swallowing hard I said, "Yes, James I know. How do you feel about that?"

"Not good. I'm the only grandchild; I'm his grandson."

His eyes held my gaze as if pleading for a magical solution to this enormous problem.

I reached over and touched his shoulder. He began slowly swinging his legs back and forth, feet unable to reach the floor from the big chair.

I asked gently, "James, what is the hardest thing about all this for you?"

"Well, that I won't have him around to teach me things. He's a teacher, you know. He got me a microscope for my birthday and a chemistry set for Christmas."

Suddenly he seemed to have a look into the future, six months ahead, to Christmas. The little seer with the box of doughnuts hung his head.

"Are you thinking about Christmas this year?"

He nodded yes. With his head still lowered he said, more to the doughnut box than to me,

"He'll die before Christmas, won't he?"

"Yes, James. He's very sick."

We sat quietly.

Finally, I said, "How would you feel about drawing some pictures?"

"That'd be O.K. I can draw fairly well."

"I'm sure you can," I smiled.

"What would you like me to draw?" he asked with interest.

"How would you feel about drawing three pictures? One of your Grandfather last year."

"Pap. I like to call him Pap," he said firmly.

"Yes, fine, Pap; one picture of him the way he was last year, one picture the way he is this year, and a picture of what he'll be like next year."

"Got it," he said. "By the way, do you have any of those liquid colored pens?"

"No, James, but I have a few colored magic markers and some different colored pencils."

"OK," he said. "I'll make the best of it."

Smiling, I sat at my desk while he worked.

After twenty minutes he finished and brought the pictures to me. He laid the drawings before me, in sequence, then sat in the chair beside my desk.

"Would you be more comfortable sitting in our other chairs," I inquired.

"No, thank you, this is fine."

He waited patiently as I glanced over the drawings.

"These are quite good, James, would you explain each one please?"

"Well, this first picture is my Pap feeding the birds and you can see this bright red cardinal eating the bird seed."

"You've drawn a smile on your Grandfather's face."

"That's because he's happy when he feeds the birds. I mean when he used to feed them."

"Since he's unable to feed the birds now have you taken over the job?"

"No, but I bet I could!"

"I bet you could. Now, tell me about this second picture."

"Well, that's the one you said to draw about what he's like this year."

"Yes."

"Right now, this year, he's sick, in bed. So I have the covers on him and this string has a bell on it so he can call my Grandmother if he needs help."

"I see. What kinds of things would he need help to do?"

"Oh, maybe wash his face or something."

"You've colored his face here very orange or dark yellow," I nonchalantly commented, feeling intuitively that this might be the basis of his reluctance to visit.

"Yes, that's how he looks now. I spent a lot of time getting his face the right color."

"What do you think is making his face that color," I asked.

"I don't know for sure, but I think it has something to do with the cancer, and, do you know what else?; sometimes he doesn't know who I am and he gets mixed up and things and he yells out loud and even tries to get out of bed and Grandma gets nervous and upset."

Once again his eyes held mine, imploring me to fix his world.

"Tell me about your third drawing, the way your Pap is going to be next year, and then I'll draw a picture for you that I think will help you feel better."

"This is a cemetery. I think the one beside the church, and here is his tombstone with his name. I didn't know what year he was born but he's 66 now and I subtracted 66 from 1981 and so that makes the year 1915. I put 1915 – 1981 in black pencil like they carve into a tombstone."

"You're a clever fellow," I said, squeezing his shoulder. "These pictures are very good and you explained them to me quite well. Let me draw something for you."

He leaned closer, eager to participate.

"James, your Grand, ah, your Pap, has cancer in his liver." I drew a primitive picture and included an invasive tumor.

"The job of his liver, and yours and mine is to filter poisons from blood. This is an important job because when the filter is blocked with cancer cells the poisons ride along in his bloodstream and go through his brain. He's not supposed to have any poison in his brain, but now he does and that's why, sometimes, your Pap is confused and doesn't know where he is."

He sat motionless, attention undivided.

"Also, James, the liver has some liquid in it called bile and it's job is to help absorb certain fat particles. But the bile is not able to work because of the cancer cells so that liquid, which is yellow, gets dumped into your Grandfather's bloodstream and it circulates throughout his body turning his skin orange."

"I understand now!" he said. "Boy, I bet Grandma will feel a lot better after I explain all this to her."

"I'm sure she will, James. Do you feel a lot better?"

"Yes. I very much do!"

"I'm going to be visiting your Grandparents this afternoon, around three o'clock. If you'd like, you're welcome to join me."

Without hesitation he said an unequivocal "yea, sure."

As we walked to the office door he slipped his arm around my waist.

"My Pap is really lucky to have you for his friend."

Swallowing hard I replied, "Your Pap is lucky to have you as his Grandson, James."

"OK, thanks, see ya later."

I had been sitting by his Grandfather's bed for about half an hour when I heard James and his mother enter the house. Although I felt good about our earlier session with the drawings I was still unsure about his actual recovery regarding entering the dying man's room.

As I waited I looked at Mr. Weaver. He lay quietly. His color was bright yellow and made more vivid by contrast to the clean, white linens. His grey hair was neatly combed, parted on the side with a tuft-like cowlick defiantly sticking up.

His yellow-orange hands rested at his side and occasionally would clench weakly into fists.

I wondered if he too was enraged with the indignity of his fine mind being poisoned with liver toxins. Surely, deep inside him, he knew his teaching was finished, but never completed.

My peripheral vision suddenly caught the blond head of James peering around the corner of the door.

I said nothing.

Slowly he moved into the room.

I looked at him and smiled, hoping to give gentle encouragement.

A few more steps brought him next to the large, over-stuffed chair in which I was sitting.

He stood quietly beside me eying his Grandfather warily.

Satisfied that all was temporarily well he eased himself upon the wide arm of the chair and put his head on my shoulder.

He smelled like sunshine.

My eyes filled with tears.

I said nothing. I couldn't.

After a few moments he slipped off the chair and stood near the head of the bed.

With slight hesitation he touched the yellow hand of the man who loved to feed birds.

"Pap," he whispered. "It's me."

Mr. Weaver opened his eyes, yellow with jaundice. I watched him struggle to make his fine mind serve him one more time.

He recognized the boy!

"James," he stammered.

The battle of fear over I rose to leave the room.

A very steady, strong ten-year old voice said, "I love you, Pap."

Paralyzed with anticipation I waited, heart pounding in my throat, fearful that his Pap would not recognize him.

And then I heard it, and James heard it, and Almighty God heard it.

"I love you, too."

Late that night, when the sky was dark, Mr. Weaver quietly died. There were no more confused, violent hours following his Grandson's visit.

James was asleep, dreaming, in his room with the books, and the microscope and his chemistry set.

I hope he learned one last lesson from his Pap. That all of us fear something and that having the courage to confront that fear might not always result in conquering it but it teaches us that it's better to try, and fail, than never to try at all.

RONNIE

H E WAS THIRTY-FOUR, SIX-FOOT, ONE-HUNDRED EIGHTY pounds, blond-haired and had a slight fever. That was last year.

This year he was thirty-five, six-foot, and weighed ninety-nine pounds and had lymphosarcoma.

His wife called my office, crying. She was standing by his bed in the Hershey Medical Center wanting to take him home to die but was worried about the effect his presence would have on their children, Jeff, age 7, and Susie, 5.

"Have the children seen their father in this emaciated condition?" I asked.

"Oh, yes. They visit everyday."

"What does your husband want, Terri?"

"Well, today he's not able to respond but a few days ago he was quite adamant about dying in his own home."

She was crying harder.

"Terri, give me your address and I'll meet you there at five. Since he's not a patient in our hospital, I can't leave until my day is completed."

"I understand, Joy. I'm just so grateful that you're going to help, thank you."

"I'm planning on being supportive throughout this whole time, but I certainly can't do it alone. Ask one of the nurses to call the Social Service Department for you. They're experts at coordinating home nurses and a bed and physician's orders and all those little details. Now, give me directions to your house, and remember, I'm not such a good navigator."

I will never require consultation of my map again. Within five days I had made twelve visits and, literally, could find my way there in the dark.

The problem was his intractable pain. Around his spinal cord, behind his stomach was a large tumor pressing on many sensitive nerves.

Nothing gave relief.

I too felt painful when my telephone would ring at eleven thirty at night, and Terri would apologetically plead for me to come help while in the background I could hear Ronnie's screams.

We tried relaxation techniques, music, injections of morphine into his wasted buttocks and we tried prayer. Still he screamed.

He had been home a week when Terri decided to readmit him to the hospital.

"We just can't take it anymore, Joy. *He* can't take it anymore."

Unable to suggest an alternative, I agreed.

While in the hospital his physicians administered morphine intravenously. He slept constantly. The medical and nursing staff were pleased. Terri was relieved. I said,

"There's got to be a state of in-between. This isn't how he needs to be, just to be painfree! What in God's name can we do to get him fairly comfortable but still able to interact with his family, at home, during these final days?"

The following morning I attended a private brunch at Presbyterian Hospital in Philadelphia with Dame Cicely Saunders from St. Christopher's Hospice in Sydenham, near London. As the Medical Director she related to us Thuratology Specialists the efficacy of a wonderful drink called Brompton's Mix.

The concoction contained Heroin powder, cocaine, honey, and whiskey mixed into chloroform water. I couldn't imagine how my sweet, little Baptist and Methodist ladies would accept this new medicine but it was giving dying British the comfort they deserved.

After speaking briefly of Ronnie's condition to Dr. Saunders she highly recommended Bromptons but reminded me of the illegality of Heroin in the United States.

"You'll have to substitute morphine." She said.

"How much, please?" I inquired.

"As much as it takes, dear. Always remember that. There is no rule book for comfort because everyone's pain is his own. Don't hold back. Use as much as it takes."

It took three days to juggle the ingredients to find the magic amount.

Smiling and wincing only slightly Ronnie was carried from the ambulance into his living room where his bed waited as a throne.

There were more difficult times but for the most part the next month went well, with picnics on the living room floor and a birthday party on his bed. He was certainly exhausted and much more painful after these rousing events but he chose to take the consequences rather than let a minute of life escape him.

Susie, his five year old daughter, would don her little nurse's cap and walk in from the kitchen carrying a large tray, in the middle of which sat a one ounce plastic cup of yellow liquid.

"OK, Daddy, it's time for your Broctums!"

Terri and I would smile and recall the fear she once had of exposing the children to death.

Jeff had asked her the night before as she tucked him in bed,

"Mom, when is Daddy going to get better?"

"He's never going to get better." Terri said.

"Is he going to die?"

"Yes, Jeff, he is. The doctors are not able to make Daddy well again."

"After he dies will we have to move away?"

"No, we'll still be a family, right here."

"OK, Mom, goodnight."

It was the last week in August when Ronnie began to slip rapidly. I felt death could occur that night and gave that information to Terri.

"What do you think we ought to do about the children?" She asked.

"Well," I sighed. "According to what I've seen and heard

these past twelve weeks, I think they're experienced enough to decide for themselves."

We sat outside at the picnic table and drank lemonade.

"Kids," Terri said, "Joy is a nurse and she works with lots of people who have cancer. She examined Daddy this morning and said he might die tonight. If he starts to die would you want us to tell you so you could be with him?"

"Oh, yes," said Susie. "Even wake me up, Mommy."

Jeff, more pragmatic, said to me,

"What's it going to be like? Will it be scary or anything?"

"I don't think so, Jeff. You know how much your Dad is sleeping now and how he doesn't answer when we call his name?"

"Yeh."

"Well, I think he's just going to die very quietly. He's not painful, like he was, and we'll all be here together."

"OK. Wake me, too, Mom, for sure."

About 2:45 a.m. Susie and Jeff and Terri and her mother along with Ronnie's mother gathered in and on and around his bed as he died.

Later, after his broken body was removed Susie climbed up on the couch beside me and showed me a picture of Ronnie taken two years ago.

"This is what my Daddy looks like now! He's in Heaven and he got his good body back."

I hugged her in her pink, crinkle-crepe summer pajamas and kissed the scar on her little arm where she fell and cut it when she was only three years old.

Terri had fainted in the emergency room during the suturing.

I felt proud for this family who never watched medical shows on TV and waited for the mother cat to carry out her own delivery sequestered safely out in the garage.

They had all come such a long way and I knew they had a difficult road ahead of them. But they had said yes to death and were strengthened by and through that experience.

And now they were saying yes to life.

HANGING ON OR LETTING GO

I WAS A STUDENT IN MY FIRST YEAR AT HARRISBURG AREA Community College. As a Licensed Practical Nurse, I felt fairly well-experienced and quite comfortable working weekends.

Things were sometimes a bit hectic. Two nurses had called in sick and our medical/surgical floor seemed over-flowing with patients who required two or more nurses just to turn them from one side to another.

I was in a four-bed ward, anxiously setting patients up for their dinner trays. One of the four individuals in the room, a little old lady, who's name I can't recall, was physically able to sit out of bed, in a chair, to eat her evening meal. To simplify tasks for myself, I was taking advantage of her physical strength and urged her to get out of bed.

"Don't!" she said. "Leave me alone."

"All I want you to do is sit here on the chair to eat dinner."

"I don't want any dinner. Leave me alone. I'm going to die, and I don't want to be sitting in that chair when I'm going to do it."

"You're not going to die," I chided. "Here, let me help you swing your legs out."

"Don't, I said! Let me alone. I'm going to die. I told you. Just let me die in bed!"

"And I told you you're not going to die, at least not today, so please sit here in your chair and I'll bring supper."

Mumbling, she acquiesed.

I brought her tray and prepared the food in front of her.

Bustling up and down the hall I would glimpse in at her. She was eating. I smiled smugly.

Twenty minutes later, while collecting trays, I entered her room and found her slumped back in the chair. The silverware was neatly placed across her plate, and she was dead.

During the many years that followed, I remembered this woman's words, and I learned that we probably can choose the moment to give up the ghost or, as in the following story, when to hang on, despite incredible physical odds.

Laura had cancer of the uterus. The malignancy had spread throughout her pelvis. She was so pale it was hard to see the features of her face. She appeared to be fading into the white pillow. I had been visiting her for a week or ten days and, during that time, she had shared many feelings about her impending death. It was amazing that she was even alive. Daily she was transfused with two or three pints of blood and daily she would ooze the same amount from her vagina.

"Laura, don't you think it's time I called your son?"

"No, Joy, I'll tell you when."

Several days later, I asked again. "Laura, is it time for me to call Bobby?"

"No, I'll tell you."

Late one Friday afternoon, I sat by her bed while blood dripped slowly into her vein. "Laura, Monday is the 4th of July, so I'm going to be off duty for the long weekend. I'm worried that you might not live until I return and it would be too late to call Bobby."

"You're right, Joy. Call him now."

I placed the call to Colorado and told him about his mother's serious condition. Before leaving the hospital, I asked Laura what had made her decide that now was the right time.

"See, Bobby doesn't have enough money to fly here to Pennsylvania. It takes him three days to drive from Denver. I didn't want him to drive all the way here just to visit me, then drive all the way back, then have to turn around and drive all the way here for my funeral. It's time now."

He arrived late Monday night. They visited together for only an hour and then she died. She timed it just right.

So did another patient named Colonel Wooden. He was 58 and retired from the Air Force. His wife was legally blind, able to function, but unemployable and unable to drive.

His diagnosis of oat-cell carcinoma threw him into deep despair. Although his prognosis was one year, he rapidly declined and died within three months.

I recall sitting on his bed relaying my observations.

"You know, Colonel, I've always been straight with you."

"Yeh, and I appreciated it."

"Well, I spoke with Dr. Grant again and he told me the cancer isn't bad enough to be killing you this fast. Have you just plain given up?"

"It's like this," he said weakly. "I watched my first wife suffer and die with cancer. I don't want to put my beautiful Betty through that. I figure the most loving thing I can do for her is to finish this up soon. Also, she'll have some of our savings left to live on after I go. She can't work, you know, and I don't want her throwing money away taking care of me for the next year. Then what's she got? No husband and no money. Then what's going to happen to her? Maybe lose the house I worked so hard to get? Nope, I know exactly what I'm doing."

There was no reasoning with him. He died and she crumbled. (Read more about Lucille in Chapter 22).

This last case is not to be confused with the idea that if a patient is told the truth about his diagnosis he'll give up. The Colonel was not giving up; he was deliberately choosing to die sooner for, what was to him, an altruistic motivation. He exhibited no depression. He had a purpose to his work.

Another fine example of dying within a structured time framework is about a sensitive young man who needed to die to provide a tax break for his father.

"You'll just love him, Joy, but he's a real brain."

"How old is he, Barb?"

"I think early thirties. He hasn't been in the unit more than a few days. You'll just love him!"

Indeed I did. A non-smoker, Tim was newly diagnosed with lung cancer. He was transferred from ICU to a semiprivate room. I learned he was a lawyer, too brilliant for this world. He shared with me a self-fulfilled prophecy that he, like jesus Christ and Alexander the Great, was destined to die at thirty-two. Actually, his prognosis was several years, but that time span did not fit in with his plans of completion. Like the other great men before him, he needed to die at age thirty-two.

In the beginning of our relationship, we tried to impress each other with all the books we'd read. He threw a lot of big names around and I matched him with a list of my own. All of this was groundwork, feeling our way until we slowly began sharing common interests like fine art work and chocolate milkshakes. I would run down to the snack shop and buy us a shake, then sit and talk for hours. Sometimes the conversation would be about world affairs or artists or classical music. Occasionally he would slip in some of his feelings.

He went home for Thanksgiving, but was readmitted through Emergency late in the night. His blood levels were dangerously low, and it was unbelievable that he could even stand. Several days later, his physician informed me that he had developed a deadly blood disorder. His prognosis was three weeks.

I was sitting by his bed, holding his hand while he received four transfusions. At the same time, his belly was being tapped of free blood that had accumulated. He was deathly ill. He looked over at me and shared the following:

"My Dad was a traveling salesman and one day when I was about ten years old, I ran to his car to greet him with a kiss. He held me away from him and said, 'You're a young man now. From today on, we'll just shake hands.'" He closed his eyes and dismissed me with a way of his ghostly pale hand.

The next day, he paged me to come to his room. I stopped off first for two chocolate shakes, then bounded up the stairs to his floor. I was greeted by Tim's brother Art who was standing in the doorway with a grin on his face and a huge package in his arms. He thrust it at me, and I almost dropped the milkshakes.

"Go on," Tim said, managing a weak smile, "hurry and open it."

All right, Counselor, you don't have to get pushy." Excitedly, I tore off the wrapping to reveal an exquisite portrait of a woman seated in a Morris chair.

"Her name is Velma," Tim told me, "and she once hung in the Mellon Gallery. She was painted by Carolin McCreary. I bought it from an antique dealer."

"Oh, Tim it's just beautiful! Thank you very much."

"Well, I wanted you to have it."

"I love it. I'll always cherish it from you."

He fell back onto his pillows, but this time did not dismiss me.

The next day, he became very insistant that I take him upstairs to the nursery. His blood count was unbelievably low. Weak and frail, I could hardly manage his six foot frame into the wheelchair. I took him through a maze of corridors into the elevator, and up to the maternity floor. He sat outside the large nursery window and focused on a little eight pound baby girl. He held himself up and watched her for close to an hour. I was halfway down the hall, watching him. I just stood back, grieving for him that he had never fit in—never would—father a babe. He drooped and I ran to catch him. He said, "I think she saw me." "I'm sure she did, Tim."

I took him back to his room, he was exhausted, so I left him alone. I was never sure that he wouldn't die any minute—that's how bad he was. So the weekend had passed, and on Monday, he had very excitedly called my office, saying "There's a surprise. Can you come down?" I said, "Yes." "The Third Man" was being shown on cable t.v. He was a t.v. nut, which I found incompatible with his wisdom and intelligence. He just loved game shows; everything on television. It was always on, and he was always watching it. He asked me if I would watch it with him.

"I never thought I'd live to watch it one more time."

I said, "I'll spring for milkshakes, but the next time is your turn." He knew it was the last time. I lay down on the bed beside him, and he could hardly draw on the straw of the milkshake. He made it through that movie. A nurse stuck her head in to take his temperature, and just about dropped the whole tray of thermometers because I was lying in bed with him. I didn't care; I loved him.

I asked if he was afraid to die.

He said, "Not at all." I assured him that as a spirit he would find it incredible, the neat things that his mind could do and the challenges—he'd love it.

"You know, Tim, we've been going round and round on this argument about whether or not we possess souls. I certainly don't mean to be smug but I'm so positive about it I just have to be able to say I told you so!"

"Whatever would you propose?" he inquired winking.

"I have a bust of Beethoven on my mantle. *When,* not if, but *when* you cross over I'd like you to turn the bust so I know you made it."

"No deal, Ufema," he smirked. "When you're gone, you're gone, and that's it."

I said, "Okay."

Sunday I was called in to see a patient whose child was burned and died. After I worked with her, I went to see Tim. When I got to the door, his father was sitting at the bedside, reading the *Washington Post.* Tim was almost comatose, and I saw his Dad lean over and kiss him. I went in and told Tim that it was I and gave him a kiss too.

"Don't forget to turn the Beethoven bust."

"I will," he whispered, "360 degrees."

He died quietly about an hour later, at age 32. I'll never know if he's turned Beethoven in an entire circle, but Velma is on display in my home, and I occasionally catch her giving me a haunting smile.

GRIEVING

GRIEVING IS SO MUCH MORE DIFFICULT WHEN THERE CAN BE NO closing, no final goodby to finish up. Even when we do have a body and a funeral with helpful rituals, grief still takes a toll of the human heart.

Colonel Wooden laid down and died to spare his wife from any burden. In a sense, he did it so quickly and in such an isolated way that his wife missed out on any opportunity to find completeness in their relationship.

My first bereavement visit to Mrs. Wooden, four weeks after his death, revealed a huge house, manicured lawn, a three-car garage and an American flag at halfmast blowing from a large, white pole.

Although I was expected, my entering was delayed by the releasing of numerous dead-bolts, gravity latches, locks and chains after I rang the bell.

Unlike many recent widows, Lucille was not in her bathrobe. Beautifully coiffed and dressed in a silken kimona she stood back and invited me to come into her home.

We sat at either end of a very large table. Lucille picked at the food she had prepared for lunch then suddenly jumped up and exclaimed, "Would you like to see the rest of the house?"

"Of course," I mumbled, through a ham salad sandwich.

We went from one large room to another. One bedroom after another, all prepared and made up as if awaiting guests. She quietly closed each door, sealing the rooms like mausoleums, never to be disturbed, never to be touched with life.

She saved their bedroom till last. The bed was round and took up most of the room. On it was a velvet spread, with a design of red and white hearts. Between the pillows lay a folded American flag, presented to Lucille in honor of the Colonel's status as a veteran. Upon the flag was a spray of red roses, four weeks old and very dead.

Various medals were pinned to the pillows with ten or twelve pictures of her husband on display all over the walls, bureaus, and nightstands. She had converted their bedroom into a monument. His Air Force uniform hung in state outside the closet door. Plastic-coated newspaper obituaries were propped up throughout the powder room. Red foil hearts were pasted to the mirror. Stuffed animals with red and white simulated fur stood, holding hearts, as a protective guard of little soldiers, attentive, like her, awaiting one more inspection by the Colonel.

The tour completed she handed me my coat and thanked me for coming. I was dismissed. She was not interested in any discussion.

I telephoned a few weeks later. Lucille told me that she couldn't stand being alone in the house and was joining friends on a cruise to the Carribean.

The escape may help but one day she's going to have to return and dispose of the roses.

I want to point out that her behavior is normal grieving for one or two months after death. If her home would remain this way after a year I would think Lucille might require more serious attention regarding her bereavement.

With the return of the dead soldiers from Vietnam, many women were forbidden to view their husbands' bodies. Weeks or more may have elapsed between the time of death and the arrival of the body to a small town in the United States. Funeral directors, thinking they were protecting wives and children from emotional trauma advised against viewing.

In my opinion the worst thing that can happen is not looking at a cold, torn-up body that has been dead for five weeks. The agony lies in *not knowing for sure*. The tag on the coffin may say it is her husband's body inside, but she hasn't been convinced. We can and do recover from losing someone we adored but that recovery may never even begin unless we are positive the individual is actually dead.

The worst thing that can happen, and frequently does, is the haunting in the hearts of the survivors. As painful as death can be it is worse to worry that a loved one is wounded somewhere in the jungle, or captured and being held prisoner. Even death is sometimes safer.

A friend was notifed that the small plane which her brother was piloting over a remote territory in Alaska crashed. He and his passenger were killed.

It took a week for the bodies to be located then another few days to be shipped to Fairbanks then to Montana for burial. The kindly mortician did not suggest viewing, even for my friend and her Mother. Knowing the value of verification my friend insisted. Of course her brother did not look natural or like he was sleeping. Tragically, he was dead; and he looked dead. His body was badly bruised and broken, but she knew for certain that it was her sweet brother. She said it would have been worse worrying that he might have had a brain concussion and be wandering around the forest or pinned beneath the plane wreckage as it burst into flames. Knowing was a release.

It may be a difficult and sometimes over-whelming task for survivors to be assertive about viewing the dead body. It is my opinion, and supported by other literature, that seeing our loved one, dead, is beneficial in assisting us through our grief work.

IT'S RISKY TO BE REAL

THE SKIN HORSE HAD LIVED LONGER IN THE NURSERY THAN any of the others. He was so old that his brown coat was bald in patches and showed the seams underneath, and most of the hairs in his tail had been pulled out to string bead necklaces. He was wise, for he had seen a long succession of mechanical toys arrive to boast and swagger, and by-and-by break their main-springs and pass away, and he knew that they were only toys, and would never turn into anything else. For nursery magic is very strange and wonderful, and only those playthings that are old and wise and experienced like the Skin Horse understand all about it.

"What is REAL?" asked the Rabbit one day, when they were lying side by side near the nursery fender, before Nana came to tidy the room. "Does it mean having things that buzz inside you and a stick-out handle?"

"Real isn't how you are made," said the Skin Horse. "It's a thing that happens to you. When a child loves you for a long, long, time, not just to play with, but REALLY loves you, then you become Real."

"Does it hurt?" asked the Rabbit.

"Sometimes," said the Skin Horse, for he was always truthful. "When you are Real you don't mind being hurt."

"Does it happen all at once, like being wound up," he asked, "or bit by bit?"

"It doesn't happen all at once," said the Skin Horse. "You

become. It takes a long time. That's why it doesn't often happen to people who break easily, or have sharp edges or who have to be carefully kept. Generally, by the time you are Real, most of your hair has been loved off, and your eyes drop out and you get loose in the joints and very shabby. But these things don't matter at all, because once you are real you can't be ugly, except to people who don't understand.''

"I suppose you are Real?" said the Rabbit. And then he wished he had not said it, for he thought the Skin Horse might be sensitive. But the Skin Horse only smiled.

"The Boy's uncle made me Real," he said. "That was a great many years ago; but once you are Real, you can't become unreal again. It lasts for always.''

This excerpt from Margery Williams' *The Velveteen Rabbit* is one of my favorites. The greatest compliment for me would be for my epitaph to read "Here lies a real person." To me, being real means being honest and open, especially about my feelings. The Skin Horse might have added another facet to his description. "Being real is risky." It requires courage and it may demand standing alone. The reward is intrinsic, not having concerns about what people will think. Being real means being genuine. Ironically, most people aren't interested in working toward that goal, and they can even attempt to thwart individuals who prefer realness to petty games.

While attending college, I rented a furnished house in Mechanicsburg, Pennsylvania. It was a winterized, summer cottage beside a small river. My landlady, age 72, lived next door with her 92-year-old mother. Both were spry, and I especially enjoyed watching Selma, the mother, hitch up the pony and go for a ride in the surrey, whizzing past my window.

Each month, when I paid the rent, Selma would take me aside to renew my promise that if anything would happen to her, I would look after her daughter.

"After all, Julie, you are a nurse!"

"My name is Joy, Selma, not Julie," I would correct.

"What?" she bellowed.

"Joy. My name is Joy."

"Oh, yes. Like I was saying . . . I ain't going to be around here forever, so promise you'll take care of Virginia."

"I promise."

"Oh, thank God. You're a good girl, Julie."

We walked back through the kitchen, past the pen with the two ducks, and the box of dirt growing strange herbs.

Ginny, as she preferred to be called, handed me my receipt.

"I'm so glad to have you for a tenant, Joy. I'll never raise the rent."

"Gee, thanks, Ginny. As a starving student, I appreciate that."

As she walked with me out to the porch, she said, "Joy, you know I've got diabetes and this bad ticker, so if I should go before mother, you'd watch out for her, wouldn't you?"

"You bet, you have my word."

The spring of 1972 was delicious. I studied for finals at the edge of the river, went canoeing and swimming. Then, in June, it started raining. It rained hard for ten days because Hurricane Agnes stalled over the Eastern United States. The friendly waters of the Condogoinet turned raging. They swept away a covered bridge near Carlisle. They swept away lawn furniture and horses and a coke machine, and they swept away the porch from Ginny and Selma's house. My little place was saved by a slight incline of front yard that miraculously turned away the roaring waters.

During the demanding clean-up, Selma slipped on mud-covered concrete in the basement. She fell to the floor, fracturing her brittle, 92-year-old hip.

After major surgery and three weeks in the hospital, she was transferred to a nearby nursing home for rehabilitation. I visited her on several occasions and she was recuperating well.

Three days following my visits Ginny collapsed. A massive cerebral hemorrhage felled her beside the mailbox. Neighbors and friends called the ambulance and accompanied her to the hospital.

I had left that evening for an emergency visit to Montana and was delayed a week. Upon my return I stopped by the hospital and learned that Ginny had been transferred to the same nursing home as her mother. During the short drive there, I was hoping she had improved.

After inquiring about her location, I asked the supervisor of her condition.

"Well, as you know, the stroke caused permanent damage," she smiled, feigning concern.

"Can she communicate at all?"

"Oh, no, dear, she's a vegetable."

"I take offense at your language, madam," I bristled and walked down the hall to Ginny's room.

Music wafted from speakers in the ceiling and mingled with the faint smell of urine. It seemed unreal to hear "Strangers in the Night" being crooned by Frank Sinatra. I was visiting a woman who is no longer who she was for 72 years, not shopping at K-Mart!

I found Room 408, took a deep breath, and walked in. She was in the bed by the door. The bed by the window was empty. She was propped on her side with her back towards me. Could she, too, hear Frank Sinatra?

I walked around the bed and looked down on her. Her eyes were closed. Her gray hair was matted a bit and smelled sweaty. Her false teeth had been removed, making her mouth even more distorted. The corner of her lips drooped heavily. The spark was gone.

"Ginny," I called gently. "It's Joy."

She opened her gray eyes slowly then looked directly at me.

"It's Joy, Ginny," I said, touching her shoulder.

There was no recognition; no glimmer of acknowledgment. No memory "click" of years we shared enjoying living by the river.

Leaning over the siderail I took her hand. Speaking softly, I tried to explain.

"Ginny, you've had a bad stroke. They took you to Holy Spirit then transferred you here to Mountain View, remember? Where Selma is?"

No response, although, she appeared to comprehend. "Ginny, your mother is upstairs, in another area of the nursing home. Could you squeeze my hand if you'd like me to bring her here?"

Nothing.

"OK, I can't imagine how frustrating this must be for you. I don't want to take advantage in any way of your present condition. I want to make sure I make every attempt to communicate clearly with you about this. Maybe you don't want Selma to see you like this. Could you squeeze my hand if you don't want me to bring her here?"

Nothing.

"OK. I'm going to find out from Selma what she would like to do. Ok, Ginny?"

Nothing.

I ran up the stairs and walked into Selma's room. She was sitting in a large blue chair. On a little table, beside her Bible, was a picture of her with Ginny standing in front of the cottage I rented.

"Hi, Selma, it's Joy."

She looked up from her knitting.

"Who?"

"Joy. You know, from Willow Mill Park Road."

"Willow Mill?"

"Yes, Selma, it's Joy."

"Well, my word, it's nice to see you, Julie. How are you?"

"I'm good. How's that old hip of yours?"

"It's all right. It pains me sometimes. Listen, come closer"

I pulled up a cold, plastic chair and sat near her.

"Julie, I'm awful worried about Ginny. She hasn't visited me for about two weeks. Do you know if she's all right?"

Startled for a moment, I didn't speak.

She stared deep into my eyes, imploring an explanation.

Finally, I placed my hand over hers in the knitting.

"Selma, when was the last time Ginny visited?"

"Let's see, not last week, at all, or the week before because I've run out of clean nighties."

"Ginny had a stroke and she's a patient here, downstairs."

"Oh my good Heavens! Is she all right?"

"No, Selma, she can't talk or anything. I'm really sorry."

"Oh my good Heavens."

"If you'd like, I'll take you to her."

"Yes, oh yes, now!"

"Ok, let me grab a wheelchair. I'll be right back."

As I passed the nurses' station, I saw the supervisor with whom I had conversed earlier about Ginny. Whispering to a nurse with a cap from Polyclinic Hospital, she was pointing at Selma's room.

Returning with the wheelchair, I stopped at the desk. The nurse was alone.

"Excuse me, I just want you to know I'll be taking Selma downstairs."

"Are you a member of the family?" she asked.

"No, just a friend," I smiled.

"Well, she's already had her physical therapy. Why does she need to go downstairs?"

"To see her daughter, in room 408."

She stood up, looked around, then put her face close to mine.

"She doesn't even know her daughter is here!" she hissed.

"Yes, she does. I just told her."

"You shouldn't have done that! Now she'll be all upset."

"She's already upset because Ginny hasn't visited her. She'd worry more not knowing where she is or what might have happened to her."

"You're not *really* going to take her down there to see her daughter looking like *that*, are you?"

"Looking like what?" I put *my* face close to her.

"You know."

"No, I don't. Why don't you tell me?"

"Well, she's a vegetable."

I spun around and walked quickly towards Selma's room. The nurse called out after me, "I'm notifying the supervisor!"

I made no reply.

Bustling Selma into the wheelchair and covering her legs with a blanket, I took her past the nurses' station to the elevator.

Downstairs, in Ginny's room, I lowered the siderail and placed the wheelchair close to the bed. When Selma saw Ginny she began to cry while stroking her daughter's hair.

"Oh, my baby, my baby. What's happened to you? Oh, Honey, can you hear me. Virginia, it's mother, talk to me! Oh, my baby."

There was no response.

"Selma, even though Ginny can't speak to you, I think she can hear you and knows that you're here. The nerves coming from her brain have been damaged but the nerves going to her brain are Ok. It must be very difficult for her, and us, but we've got to talk to her and touch her just like always."

"Oh, yes, Julie, you're right."

We stayed for about an hour. After Selma kissed her "baby" daughter goodby, I stooped to speak to Ginny. Perhaps I imagined it, but her gray eyes seemed more knowing. As I took her hand, I felt an ever-so-slight squeeze.

Ginny died two days later. Selma didn't join her till a year later. I recall the picture of the two of them, and I understand now that they made each other Real "a long time ago." Also, I realize that by following through with a promise, perhaps I was a bit closer to becoming real myself.

It had been an extremely difficult day for Mr. Shope. Late in the morning he began coughing up bright blood. I skipped lunch, choosing to stay with him and clean his soiled linens.

It was a humid, August afternoon and his room was stifling. About 5:30 he lay quietly. I was hungry and exhausted. My uniform was sweaty and splattered with blood. I had changed his sheets and gown ten times. Tired, I was eager to go home and sink in a warm bath.

I stood by his bed telling him I was leaving.

Reaching up, he took my hand speaking intently, "Joy, thanks for today. Really take good care of yourself."

"I will, Mr. Shope."

Due to my fatigue his message didn't register until I got to the door. Then I knew.

With renewed strength I returned to his side and sat on his bed.

"You're not going to be here tomorrow, are you?" I asked. It was more a statement than a question.

"No."

"Well, I want to thank you for being my teacher. Do you want me to call your minister?"

"No, thanks," he smiled. "I've been prayin' all my life by myself. I reckon I can handle this last one alone, too."

"Would you like me to stay with you?"

"No. It's time for you to go and time for me to go."

I kissed his forehead.

"God bless you, Mr. Shope."

"Goodby," he said.

The next day I walked past his room. His bed was empty.

The lesson in realness here is about risking and losing face. It only took several mistakes, in rapid succession, for me to learn the value of listening to my intuition.

Although I had been trained to convert observations into a nursing diagnosis I would deny, in my "face-saving" center of my brain, what clinical messages my brain was interpreting. I had been exposed to a sufficient number of ill patients to have a working knowledge of their pending death. I was afraid to take the risk of acting on my clinical expertise plus my intuition. Consequently I would delay discussing the obvious with the patient, choosing the Scarlet O'Hara philosophy of doing it "tomorrow" only to discover there was no tomorrow, just an empty bed.

After the third transgression, I vowed it would not happen again. Today, when I observe a patient whom I feel may not live through the night I openly discuss it with the individual.

"Emily, you seem so much weaker than this morning. I'm off duty for the weekend and just in case you're not here when I return on Monday, I want you to know I care very much about you and appreciate all I've learned from you."

Patients seem to appreciate this honesty. They are fully aware that death is knocking, loudly. On few occasions I have returned on Monday to find the individual still alive. I've lost nothing.

"Emily! You're still here! Let's have a little tea and chat. What else would you teach me?"

The risk of being real can also be of great help to families. I have no hesitation in notifying family members that their loved one is slipping fast.

"Do you think we should call her son in New Jersey?"

"Yes, by all means."

If the dying person rallies for a few extra days, or as with one gentleman, a week, nothing is lost. What a luxury to get to tell Momma you love her again! What luck! She's still alive and John's plane just landed!

Becoming real doesn't happen all at once. It takes a long time.

FULL CIRCLE

I SAT RIGIDLY AS A YOUNG WOMAN IN HER BRAND-NEW, LONG sleeved nurse's uniform struggled with the high notes of "No Man Is An Island." I had delivered numerous graduation speeches but this one was different. I was speaking to the class of 1980 of the Altoona Hospital School of Nursing.

While the Director of Education introduced me, my mind wondered back twenty years to that painful day I was asked to leave the program. So many experiences had transpired since. Hopefully, growthful.

She prattled on about my publications in nursing journals, my appearance on the Phil Donahue Show, and my pioneering spirit.

"All very nice," I mused, "but, through it all, what have I learned?"

I rose to speak; my hands did not shake, my voice did not quiver, I required no consultation of my notes.

"I want to thank you students for inviting me here, this evening. I know it's appropriate for a speaker to say words like honored and privileged but I genuinely mean it when I tell you what a very special occasion this is for me."

I shared with them about that particular failing, as a young student, and I shared with them how we can utilize failings not only as stepping stones, but as memories to gentle us toward others who are slipping a bit off course, too.

"As you go forth as nurses, remember the value of integrity, honesty, and courage. I certainly don't wish to daunt the festive spirit tonight by becoming maudlin, but I simply want to remind you that one hundred years from now each of us will be a handful of dust. It doesn't matter so much *that* we die, but *how* we die, and *how* we die depends entirely on how we live. Please don't put off doing what you know is best for you or telling people you love, that you love them."

The applause, I'm sure, wasn't so much for content as it was for brevity. Regardless, I felt good about the whole thing.

Late that night, after a long drive home and the completion of barn chores, I lay in bed listening to the soothing sounds of nature's night.

The chickens were roosted safely, the ducks were nesting, and my close friend, Brandy the horse, was munching sweet hay.

In the woods a little barn owl hooted to his mate and to me. His message was simply that farms, and horses, and flowers, and people are here, now, but for me to remember they are only brief companions.

BIBLIOGRAPHY

Bluebond-Langer, M. *The Private Worlds of Dying Children.* Princeton University Press, Princeton, New Jersey, 1978.

Carnegie, D. *How to Stop Worrying and Start Living.* Simon & Schuster, Inc., New York, 1948.

Epstein, C. *Nursing the Dying Patient.* Reston Publishing Company, Inc., Reston, Virginia, 1975.

Feifel, H. (Ed) *The Meaning of Death.* McGraw-Hill, New York, 1959.

Fulton, R. *Death, Grief, and Social Recuperation, Omega 1,* 23 – 28.

Grollman, E.A. *Explaining Death To Children.* Beacon Press, Boston, Massachusetts, 1967.

Kastenbaum, R. & Aisenberg, R. *The Psychology of Death.* Springer, New York, 1972.

Kastenbaum, R. *Death, Society, and Human Experience.* The C.Y. Mosby Company, St. Louis, Missouri, 1977.

Kavanaugh, R.E., *Facing Death.* Nash Publishing, Los Angeles, California, 1972.

Grant, M.J. *Dying and Dignity — The Meaning of Control of a Personal Death.* Charles C. Thomas, Springfield, Illinois, 1974.

Kushner, H.S. *When Bad Things Happen to Good People.* Schocken Books, Inc., New York, 1981.

Kubler-Ross, E. *On Death and Dying.* MacMillan, New York, 1969.

LeShan, E. *Learning to Say Goodby: When A Parent Dies.* McMillan, New York, 1976.

Miles, M. *Annie and the Old One.* Little, Brown, Boston, Massachusetts, 1971.

Parkes, C.M. *Bereavement — Studies of Grief in Adult Life.* International Universities Press, Inc., New York, 1972.

Simonton, O. Carl, Matthew-Simonton, Stephanie, and Creighton, J. *Getting Well Again.* Bantam, New York, 1980.

Viorst, J. *The Tenth Good Thing About Barney.* Atheneum, New York, 1971.

Williams, M. *The Velveteen Rabbit.* Doubleday & Company Inc., New York, 1971.